SCRAPERS

THIS IS SCRAPERS. A VISUAL HISTORY OF MAN'S ENDEAVOURS TO REACH HIGHER AND HIGHER, THROUGH THE CONSTRUCTION OF MIND-BLOWING NEW BUILDINGS.

Zack Scott takes us on a journey from humankind's first attempts to touch the sky with their creations, to the modern masterpieces of architecture and engineering standing proudly across the globe.

From Stonehenge to the Empire State Building, the Pyramids to the Burj Khalifa, Zack shares the little-known facts and fascinating human stories behind the most incredible buildings in the world.

In gorgeous graphic style, *SCRAPERS* opens our eyes – and our minds – to these true marvels of human architecture.

for Alice

CONTENTS

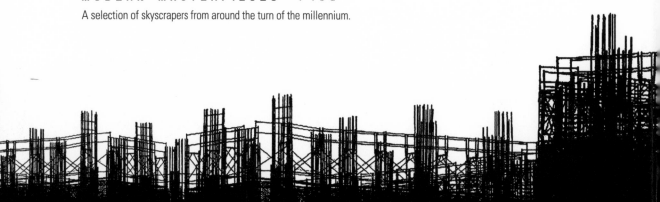

INTRODUCTION

Soaring majestically above us, seemingly defying the laws of nature, skyscrapers are truly some of the most awe-inspiring creations of the human race. Each one of them unique as a result of its time, location, cost, purpose, architect – to name but a few of the factors. Each one has a story to tell, a purpose to accomplish and an image all of its own. The shining glass towers we see today are relatively new to the world of architecture, only made possible by the accumulation of millennia's worth of knowledge and experience.

The earliest remains of human architecture date back around 7000 years to the end of the Stone Age, built by Neolithic man, so it is in this age that the book begins. To give some context to just how far our ingenuity has led us, and how far we have come, it's important to know where and how it all began. With this in mind we'll look at a selection of extraordinary historical man-made structures from around the globe, uncovering the reasons behind their construction, and the technological achievements they have accomplished. We then come to the Industrial Revolution, when one of the biggest game-changers in the history of architecture was discovered, the mass production of iron. And finally we arrive at the modern era, from the early high-rises of Chicago to the shimmering scrapers of modern-day Shanghai. This chronological tour of the world's most audacious structures takes us on a journey of discovery, laying bare the facts relating to some of the most well-known buildings, and shedding light on the reason and meaning behind them.

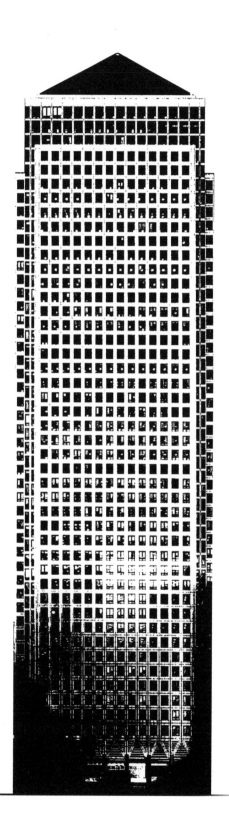

THE ROAD TO SKYSCRAPERS

Long before we had the ability to create the towers of concrete and steel that scrape the skies of today, humans strove to leave their mark on the planet. Using what was available to their given civilisation, ideas were developed, techniques were passed down through the generations, and architectural knowledge was gained... and on occasion lost. Many early civilisations have disappeared over the years, whether from war, from famine or disease, and their experiences lost to the ages. Nevertheless, as societies grew in sophistication and size, civilisations the world over would build ever more ambitious projects, pushing architectural boundaries and evolving their own styles.

A common trait among each civilisation's most important and revered structures is height, and for many reasons. The very nature of being higher grants a feeling of superiority and power over what lies below. Naturally, this is linked with primitive animal instincts – the larger the animal the more chance it has in a confrontation, and there are more advantages associated with higher ground. In contrast, a person who beholds a large, imposing structure intuitively senses its importance. A tall building also conveys its stature through the onlooker knowing what it took to accomplish. Seeing a structure the magnitude of the Egyptian Pyramids for example, especially at the time of their construction, would set the mind racing. How was it done? How many thousands of people would it have

THE GREAT
PYRAMID OF
GIZA
P12

STONEHENGE
P8

THE PARTHENON
P16

taken? The buildings themselves therefore not only serve their primary purpose, but let outsiders know that they are dealing with a sizable, and potentially more advanced, civilisation.

Some of the earliest structures on Earth date back to around 5000 BC, and consist of a variety of man-made earth mounds, simple stone tombs, underground passageways, and combinations of the three. Built by late Stone Age man, most of the structures that remain from this period seem to have ties with death, the afterlife, and some form of spirituality – themes that must have been important in their cultures. As societies grew more populous, and understanding of materials and techniques increased, buildings were able to grow in size and complexity. Religion would be at the forefront of many of the biggest buildings over the next few millennia, though not always; many monarchs would build themselves palaces, castles were built for protection, and temples serving various functions arose. The biggest upheaval in architecture would come with the Industrial Revolution. No longer was the majority of wealth owned by the church and nobility, but by entrepreneurs and industrialists. Developments leading to the mass production of iron revolutionised construction at the same time that people left the countryside for the cities, changing the face of architecture and paving the way for things to come.

ULM MINSTER
P32

PAGODA
OF FOGONG
TEMPLE
P28

PYRAMID OF
THE SUN
P20

BRIHADISVARA
TEMPLE
P24

DITHERINGTON
FLAX MILL
P36

CONSTRUCTION:
3100 – 1500BC

HEIGHT:
7.6 M

WILTSHIRE
ENGLAND

STONEHENGE

In its early days, human architecture was unable to reach great heights. The basic structures were made by Neolithic people who, with no cement or mortar, simply hauled stones of various sizes into position to create their monuments. There are many examples of this all over the world, but the most celebrated is without doubt Stonehenge.

As Neolithic man left no written records, many aspects of Stonehenge can only be speculated on. What is clearly evident, however, is that it was an extraordinary undertaking for a civilisation that had no machinery and very limited tools. The stones they used were not from the region, but sourced from afar, making the undertaking all the more impressive. Exactly how they moved such heavy rocks, without

wheels or pulleys, over wild terrain is the
subject of much debate. The most widely
accepted theory suggests they used wooden
sleds and tracks made from tree trunks, and
rafts to cross water when necessary. What
they lacked in tools and technology they
most certainly made up for in ambition, for it
was definitely back-breaking work carrying
such a huge amount of rock over such vast
distances. The famous stone circle at the

centre of the site was not actually in place
until around 2500BC, over 500 years after
the site was chosen. Initially the site was
defined by a circular ditch over 100 metres in
diameter, around which ran an earthen bank.
After the stones arrived at the site they were
rearranged to various degrees over hundreds
of years, but by 2200BC the majority had
settled in what would be their final positions.

CENTRAL TRILITHON

The central trilithon is hardly a skyscraper by today's standards,
but its size would have certainly been impressive at the time.

4.9 m

0.9 m

7.6 m

6.7 m

2.4 m

2.1 m

The central trilithon's
last remaining upright

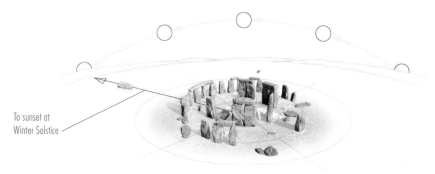

To sunset at
Winter Solstice

OBSERVATORY

Although people from this era didn't have the technical know-how to build up to the sky, they definitely had their eyes on it. Stonehenge was certainly of high astronomical importance to its creators. The position of key stones deliberately aligns with moon and sun rises and sets at meaningful days in the year. This would indicate that the site served as a celestial observatory, or at least that was one of its purposes. How this tied in with the people's religious or spiritual beliefs though remains a mystery.

Preseli Mountains
(Bluestones)

OVERLAND ROUTE

Marlborough Downs
(Sarcens)

COASTAL ROUTE

220 km

Stonehenge

Cardiff

Bournemouth

TRANSPORT ROUTES

The largest sarsen stones at the centre of the site are made from a type of sandstone found in the Marlborough Downs. They each weigh upwards of 20 tonnes and are thought to have been brought from a quarry 40 km away. The smaller bluestones, of which there were roughly 80 weighing about 2.5 tonnes each, come from the Preseli Mountains in Wales 220 km away.

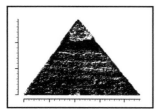

CONSTRUCTION:
2580 – 2560BC

HEIGHT:
146.7 M

GIZA
EGYPT

THE GREAT PYRAMID OF GIZA

The pyramids of Egypt, despite being built at the same time as Stonehenge, were the product of a much more advanced civilisation. The geometrically precise nature of the designs implies the architect had a greater understanding of mathematics, and the ability to realise that these designs show off the Egyptians' knowledge of construction techniques. The huge scale of the pyramids is a clear indication of a much more sizeable workforce than what would have been needed for Stonehenge, and for a long time it was supposed that it was mainly made up of slaves, though recent findings point to paid, skilled workers.

The Great Pyramid was built under the rule of Pharaoh Khufu, for whom it would serve as a tomb. No one knows for sure why Ancient Egyptians chose the form of the pyramid for their deceased rulers' burial sites. It may be that the way they point to the sky shows the soul the way to the afterlife. It could be that the shape of the pyramid is reminiscent of rays from the sun, and is therefore a symbol of their exalted Sun God. Or it might be a case of practicality – with a large base that tapers towards the peak, it is a stable construction that is likely to last. It has indeed lasted well – the Great Pyramid is the oldest of the Seven Wonders of the Ancient World, and the last one to survive.

PRECISION

The square base of the Great Pyramid is very near perfectly aligned with the compass points. The four sides are a mere twelfth of a degree off facing north, south, east and west. Looking at a plan view, it can be seen that the three main pyramids are in alignment with regards to their south-east corners, creating an angle of 51 degrees between themselves and the east-to-west lines of latitude. Interestingly, this is the same angle that the inclined walls of the pyramids adhere to, although why this angle was important to them remains a secret.

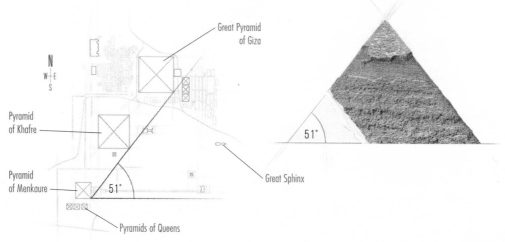

Great Pyramid
of Giza

N
W + E
S

Pyramid
of Khafre

Pyramid
of Menkaure

51°

Great Sphinx

Pyramids of Queens

51°

INTERIOR

Inside the Great Pyramid are three chambers: the subterranean chamber, the Queen's Chamber and the King's Chamber. The Pharaoh's resting place is the King's Chamber, which is lined with huge slabs of red granite and contains a sarcophagus. Narrow shafts lead from the chamber to the outer walls, which experts believe were built to allow the spirit to ascend to the heavens.

King's Chamber

Grand Gallery

Entrance

Two-storey house
(for scale)

Queen's Chamber

Subterranean Chamber

330 000 tonnes

CONSTRUCTION MATERIALS

An absolutely enormous amount of limestone was used for the pyramid. Mostly solid in construction, its mass totally dwarfs the giants of today, whose structures are usually hollow. In total there are roughly 2.3 million blocks of limestone each weighing approximately 2.5 tonnes. These were fitted at an average rate of twelve an hour, day and night, during the twenty-year construction period. Although its volume is two and a half times that of the Empire State Building, it is over eighteen times its weight.

TIME AT THE TOP

Upon its completion it became the tallest man-made structure in the world, a title it held for an unbelievable 3 800 years, when it was surpassed by Lincoln Cathedral.

5 900 000 tonnes

159.7 m

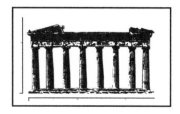

CONSTRUCTION:
447 – 438BC

HEIGHT:
13.7 M

ATHENS
GREECE

THE PARTHENON

The Parthenon, though nowhere near as tall as the Great Pyramid, still dominates the skyline of Athens, sitting high atop the Athenian Acropolis. The Acropolis is a flattish-topped rocky outcrop of land that rises 150 m above sea level in the coastal city of Athens, and at its summit is a walled citadel. The word 'acropolis' is derived from two other Greek words: *akron*, meaning the highest point or extremity, and *polis*, meaning city. It is at this vantage point that the remains of the oldest and most iconic symbol, of not only Ancient Greece, but of democracy and Western civilization, stands.

Athens was the most powerful city in Ancient Greece, home to great thinkers such as Socrates, Plato and Sophocles, as well as Hippodamus of Miletus who is the earliest historical figure associated with town planning. Ancient Greek architecture is renowned for the sense of harmony evoked by its proportions, perspective and simplicity, as well as its decoration. The Parthenon is one of the finest examples

of this. It was constructed between 447 and 438BC, although decorating it wasn't complete until 432BC. Despite being 'architecturally' a temple, it didn't serve as a place of worship or congregation; instead it housed the statue of Athena (the city's patron goddess) along with more of the city's riches. The statue was made from gold and ivory, and stood 12 m high, but it has long been destroyed.

After the age of antiquity, the Parthenon fell into different hands, being first converted into a church and in later years a mosque. It only became the ruin it is now after being hit by a cannonball during the Great Turkish War in 1687 – unfortunately the building was being used to store gunpowder and the cannonball created a huge explosion.

ENTASIS

When creating columns, the Ancient Greeks designed them so that they would be wider at the bottom with a bulge roughly a third of the way up (depending on the style), and then narrowing off towards the top. A series of straight-edged regular columns creates an optical illusion whereby the columns appear to be concave, and this effect can make them seem weak to the spectator. The subtle bulging, however, known as entasis, gives the structure the aesthetic of strength and elegance.

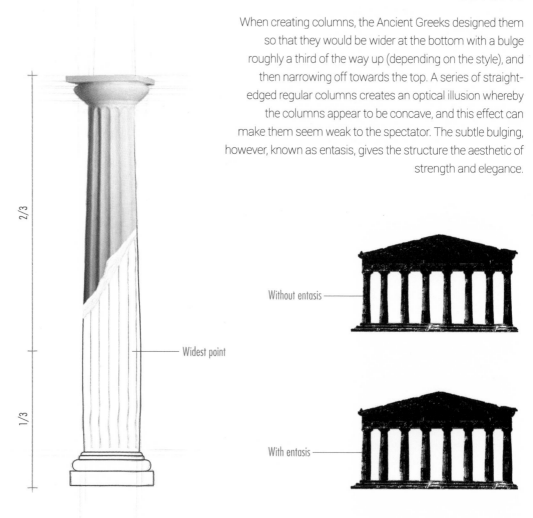

2/3

Widest point

1/3

Without entasis

With entasis

INFLUENCE

It is fair to say that the architectural style invented by the Ancient Greeks has been the most influential throughout history. It was first imitated by the Roman Empire, and then almost everyone since the end of the Dark Ages.

PANTHEON
Italy
125

PERSPECTIVE PERFECTION

The Ancient Greeks were well aware of how perspective works and how straight lines can often seem to curve from a distance, especially when looking at buildings of this scale. With this in mind, all the columns of the building lean inwards ever so fractionally. This helps give the building a lighter feeling, not too top-heavy, while it also creates the illusion of the building having perfect right angles.

Point of convergence
(not to scale)

4.8 km

1 The temple front as seen.

2 The temple front as it would appear if built without optical corrections.

3 The temple front as designed. On construction and taking into account perspective, in the flesh it would resemble A.

VILNIUS
CATHEDRAL
Lithuania
1783

SUPREME COURT
BUILDING
USA
1935

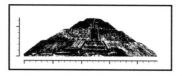

CONSTRUCTION:
100 – 200 (EST.)

HEIGHT:
65.5 m

TEOTIHUACAN
MEXICO

PYRAMID OF THE SUN

Teotihuacan is an ancient city that lies in the Valley of Mexico, 40 km north-east of present day Mexico City. The settlement was established by 100BC and grew to a population of 125 000 at its peak, making it one of the largest cities of its era in the world. Teotihuacan collapsed around AD550, which scholars thought was due to invaders looting and burning the place. However, more recently found evidence suggests that the fall of the city was due to an uprising, one that was quite possibly connected with famine.

Whatever the reason for the city's demise, it lay vacant for the next few centuries, save for a few lonely squatters. It was rediscovered by the Aztecs in the 12th century who are responsible for naming the roads and buildings we know today, such as the Pyramid of the Sun. The Aztecs believed

the pyramids at Teotihuacan to be burial places, although they were actually temples. Unfortunately, the temple constructs that used to adorn the crests of the pyramids at Teotihuacan have been destroyed, and therefore archaeologists have not been able to link the civilisation with a particular religion or deity. Although there are no chambers inside the pyramid, exploration below it has revealed a system of caves and tunnels, from which much of the building material is thought to have been mined.

The pyramid is constructed in sections of soil, rubble and rocks that are held in place by the gently sloping stone walls, with each section providing a stable base for the next. Originally, the exterior would have had a decorated, smooth finish, as it was covered in a lime-based plaster which has since been eroded.

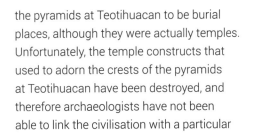

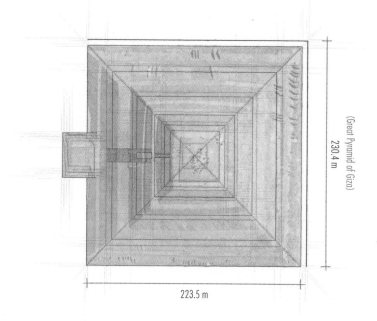

230.4 m (Great Pyramid of Giza)

223.5 m

PYRAMID COMPARISON

The Pyramid of the Sun is the third largest pyramid on the planet; its square base is in fact very nearly the same size as that of the Great Pyramid of Giza. It only reaches half the height of the Great Pyramid though due to the stepped design and shallower gradient of the walls.

146.5 m

65.5 m

PYRAMID OF THE SUN

65.5 m

PYRAMID OF THE MOON

43.0 m

SUN AND MOON

The Pyramid of the Moon was likely created sometime during the century following the Pyramid of the Sun's construction. It is situated at one end of Avenue of the Dead, the city's main road, roughly 4 km long. After climbing the 248 steps to the Pyramid of the Sun's summit, the Pyramid of the Moon, although considerably smaller, appears to be the same height as it is built on higher ground.

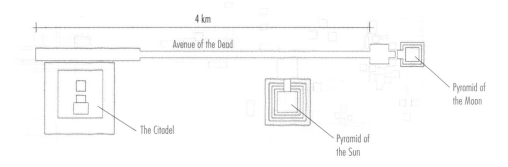

4 km

Avenue of the Dead

The Citadel

Pyramid of the Sun

Pyramid of the Moon

SACRIFICE

As well as being a bustling metropolis, Teotihuacan was also a sacred place. The temples were used for religious rituals including the sacrifice of animals and humans. Buried at each corner of the Pyramid of the Sun are the remains of children.

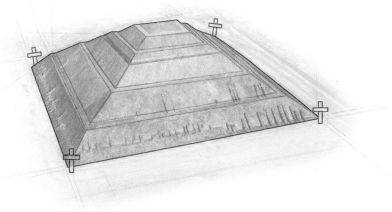

CONSTRUCTION:
1003–10

HEIGHT:
59.8 M

THANJAVUR
INDIA

BRIHADISVARA TEMPLE

From the first century AD, Hinduism began spreading across the Indian subcontinent, bringing with it new gods to replace the old. Constructs began to emerge that housed a symbol of a particular god, with space to leave offerings and perform rituals. These early Hindu places of worship were simple, usually rock-cut caves, but would often contain wall reliefs that were reminiscent of their deity's mythological adventures.

The temples developed, and by the fourth to fifth centuries AD the first free-standing temples appeared, normally crafted from wood and terracotta. Many differing trends were developing throughout the region, but over time they influenced each other, additions were built and styles started to converge. Key features that these buildings would come to possess are a portico entrance, a pillared hall that leads to the inner sanctum, and above that a tower known as the shikhara. Brihadisvara Temple at Thanjavur is a spectacular example of Hindu architecture that includes all these features.

Rajaraja I, then king of the Chola Dynasty, selected Thanjavur to be the capital of his expanding domains, as this was where he commanded his campaigns from. Rajaraja himself took a personal interest in the development of the temple, and though it was formally consecrated to the god Shiva, it would also serve to glorify its royal benefactor and his empire. Indeed, its original name was RajaRajeswara, before later being renamed to Brihadisvara.

UNPARALLELED ACCURACY

Aside from the lavish stonework and grandiose scale of the temple, Brihadisvara also excels in the accuracy of its construct. It stands at a perfect right angle, and has not subsided over an entire millennium. Why its constructors deemed it necessary to be so incredibly precise is not entirely known, nor is it known how they achieved this. Other buildings, even by more advanced societies, have not always fared so well.

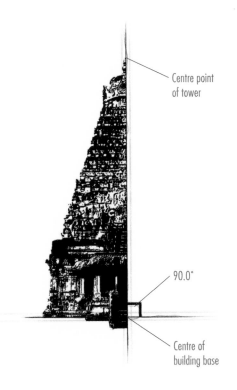

Centre point
of tower

90.0°

Centre of
building base

CROWN OF THE TOWER

One of the most striking features of Brihadisvara is its tower, crowned with a 70 tonne stone. Historians have speculated on a couple of methods of how this colossal weight could have been hauled to the temple peak.

METHOD 1
Spiralling ramp made
from earth.

TONNES OF STONE

More than 120 000 tonnes of granite were used in the
construction of Brihadisvara Temple which, incredibly, remains
upright without the use of any mortar. Instead, the stones
interlock and are laid upon each other, with the immense
weight keeping them in place. Due to the weight the walls
have to be particularly thick to support the structure.

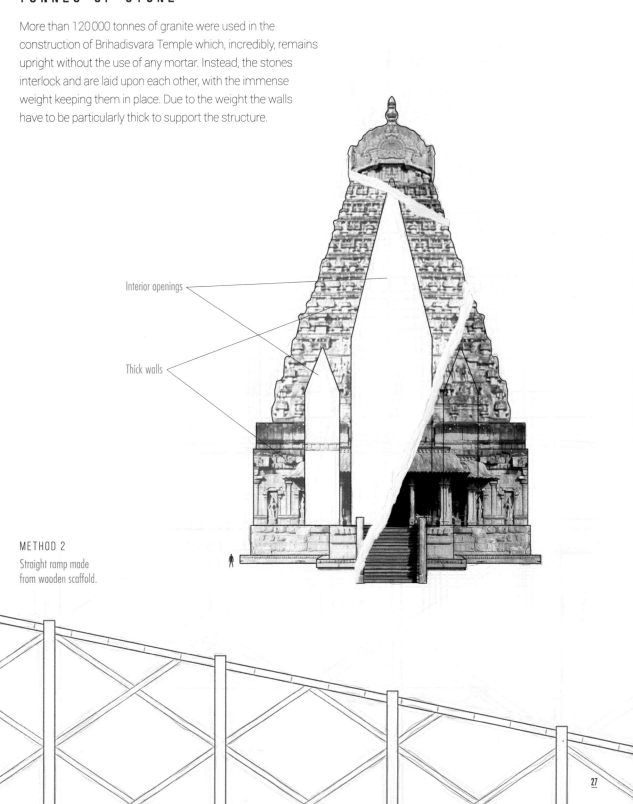

Interior openings

Thick walls

METHOD 2
Straight ramp made
from wooden scaffold.

CONSTRUCTION:
1056

HEIGHT:
67.3 M

YING COUNTY
CHINA

PAGODA OF FOGONG TEMPLE

The Pagoda of Fogong Temple is quite remarkable because, at nearly a thousand years old, it is the oldest all-wooden building in China and one of the tallest wooden constructions in the world. Just like the other buildings that we've looked at so far, it has had to withstand centuries of natural disasters, war, and wear and tear. Unlike the others it has also had to contend with rot, which will quickly ravage anything made from wood, making it all the more impressive that it still stands. The pagoda is also praised for the ingenuity of its construction techniques – not a single nail has been used, but instead the wooden components are linked together by elaborate variations of the mortise and tenon joint.

The temple was the central element of a complex of buildings built by Emperor Daozong. He chose a secluded spot, 85 km south of Datong, which was the site of his grandmother's family home. Inside the temple are many statues of Buddha, as well as portraits on the walls, the grandest of them being the 11 metre-high statue on the ground floor. As a Buddhist, the creation of this towering, elaborately designed shrine would certainly demonstrate his devotion to the cause.

BUILT TO LAST

Over the fifty years following the pagoda's construction there were seven recorded earthquakes, and surely many more have followed since but have gone undocumented. The building owes its longevity to several design attributes.

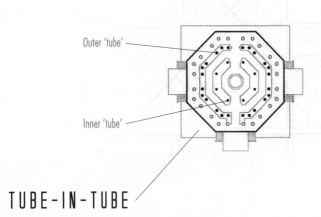

Outer 'tube'

Inner 'tube'

TUBE-IN-TUBE

The tower's structure features an inner and outer ring of pillars on each floor, with each floor's pillars aligning directly with those on adjacent floors. The connections between the pillars have drawn comparisons with the way modern skyscrapers are made, a sort of 'tube-in-tube' design that helps to spread loads.

TAPERING

The pillars on each floor slant inwards ever so slightly, and the top of each pillar is positioned half of its diameter towards the building's centre in relation to its base. The tapering of the building also, incidentally, creates the illusion of it being taller than it is.

ELASTICITY

The use of multiple dougong gives the building some elasticity, which is key to buildings surviving excessive shaking.

DOUGONG

The variants of mortise and tenon joints used in traditional Chinese architecture are known as *dougong*. Dougong help spread the load at the wooden joints, unlike nails which concentrate the load in much smaller areas. There are fifty-four variants of dougong on this building, more than any other of the era.

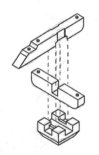
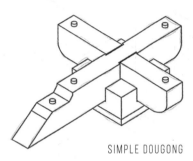

SIMPLE DOUGONG

COMPARISON WITH TODAY

Not just a spectacle of the time, the Pagoda of Fogong Temple stands as high as a modern-day twenty-storey building.

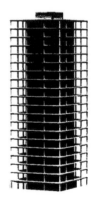

CONSTRUCTION:
1377–90

HEIGHT:
161.5 m

ULM
GERMANY

ULM MINSTER

Ulm Minster has spent most of its existence under construction, having seen many architects come and go over the centuries it took to complete. In spite of this the end result is a striking example of Gothic architecture, and a steeple that is taller than any other church in the world.

The original parish church at Ulm was situated outside of the city walls, which caused problems for its citizens due to the turmoil of the medieval period. Ulm's inhabitants desired a new church inside the city walls, so much in fact, that they funded the construction themselves without the aid of church, royal or noble money.

Construction began in 1377 on what was to be a Roman Catholic church, and over the next 150 years, steady progress was made with occasional tweaks and adjustments to the original plan. However, in 1543, shortly after the congregation converted to Protestantism, work was halted on the church due to a combination of political, economic and religious factors. Work did not recommence until 1844, and the steeple reached its full height on completion in 1890, making it the tallest building in the world at the time – until it was surpassed by Philadelphia City Hall in 1901.

Although it is sometimes referred to as Ulm Cathedral because its size understandably gives the impression of great importance, it was never the seat of a bishop and so the church is not a cathedral. Cathedrals had been springing up all over Europe since the Roman Empire, and just like them Ulm Minster became the focal point of its town, a defining characteristic, a place to unite people under the same ideology, a building whose grand scale and beauty would inspire the masses, and an unmissable beacon of the town's identity.

169.3 m

161.5 m

WALK TO THE TOP

Although the Washington Monument is about 8 m taller than Ulm Minster, it is far easier to get to the top. Ulm has no lift and therefore, if you want to reach the pinnacle of the steeple, you must take the 768 steps.

LARGE ORGAN

As well as the elegantly carved pews, magnificent sculptures and ornate stained glass windows, the church is home to a huge pipe organ. The organ was installed in the late 16th century, and is made from 8 900 individual sections of pipe that contribute to it once holding the record of being the largest organ in the world. In 1763 it was recorded that Mozart himself played it.

28.3 m

BEFORE THE 20TH CENTURY

Upon completion in 1890, Ulm Minster became the world's tallest building, but before the turn of the century it would be surpassed in height four more times. Here are the five tallest structures completed by 1900.

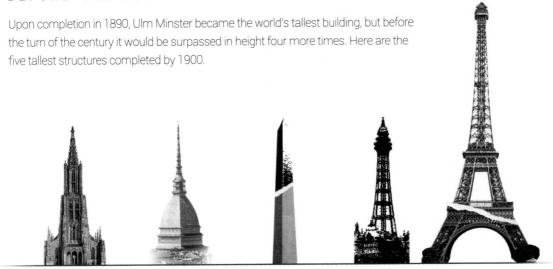

ULM MINSTER	MOLE ANTONELLIANA	WASHINGTON MONUMENT	NEW BRIGHTON TOWER	EIFFEL TOWER
161 m	167 m	169 m	173 m	300 m

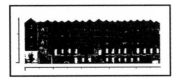

CONSTRUCTION:
1796–7

HEIGHT:
16.2 m

SHREWSBURY
ENGLAND

DITHERINGTON FLAX MILL

From its outward appearance Ditherington Flax Mill is quite unassuming, a five-storey brick building that overlooks a nondescript suburb of Shrewsbury. However, it hides its prestige well – as the world's first entirely iron-framed building it is often considered to be the 'grandfather of skyscrapers'.

Flax mills in the 18th century were highly prone to catching fire. Typically, they were brick-walled buildings with wooden floors supported by timber beams, that over time became saturated with oil from the machines. Along with the combustible fibres from the yarn being spun there, and the use of oil lamps, it is no surprise that many of these burnt to the ground. Charles Bage, a local engineer, sought to overcome this problem by eliminating flammable materials from the design of industrial buildings. He proposed a new design, and with backing from his business partners work began on

the Ditherington mill in 1796, with it up and running the following year. Well ahead of his time, Bage paved the way for a new type of building, and created one of the country's most architecturally significant structures. Over the years, several more iron-framed buildings were built at the site as business expanded. In 1886, however, the building ceased being used to spin flax and some years later was converted into a malthouse, from which it gets its more popular local name, 'The Maltings'. There was less need for natural light with this new role, and most of the 290 cast-iron windows were removed, and the openings bricked up. The building continued to serve as a malthouse until 1987 but has remained derelict ever since.

LOAD-BEARING WALLS

Unlike modern skyscrapers the mill's thick brick walls support
most of the building's weight. These days, tall buildings transmit
much of their weight to the ground through their steel framework.

DITHERINGTON FLAX MILL

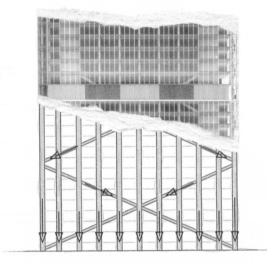

MODERN SKYSCRAPER

BIG THINGS HAVE SMALL BEGINNINGS

Gauged by later standards Ditherington Flax Mill is no giant, but the ideas and
principles its structure embodies would develop and grow.

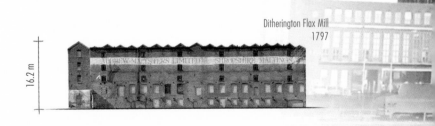

Ditherington Flax Mill
1797

16.2 m

FLOOR SPACE

Although the building was the largest flax mill at the time, its dimensions are not big by today's standards. The working area of the mill, spread over its five floors, is only 2 880 square metres, which is roughly half the area of a football pitch.

53 m

11 m

125 m

Wolfsburg Volkswagen Plant
1938

SKYSCRAPER BOOM

There is some disagreement over which building is 'the first skyscraper', as the title depends on what criteria are used. The Equitable Life Building in Manhattan, for example, was the first tall office block with an elevator, and the nearby Produce Exchange used iron in advanced ways within its framework. It is Chicago's Home Insurance Building that usually gets the recognition, however. The ten-storey block's use of steel incorporated with the iron framework made the structure so strong that it weighed only a third of a comparably sized masonry building, setting precedents in skyscraper construction. Unfortunately, the building was demolished in 1931 to make way for a bank.

My view is, it's not important which building gets the recognition. In a process of subtle design changes and slight structural differences, can there really be a definitive first? Even in the case of the Home Insurance Building, it did not use metal throughout its frame — some of the ground-floor structure is traditional masonry. What can be pinned down, though, is where and when the skyscraper movement started, the beginning of what we today recognise as skyscrapers.

Initially, it was Chicago that led the way in skyscraper construction. The Great Chicago Fire of 1871 had destroyed a considerable swathe of the city, and in the aftermath the land was divided into a grid network of large plots. New city-wide ordnances prohibited construction with wood, and with land being precious in the centre of town, building upwards made sense. It is in these circumstances that Chicago saw its first wave of tall, fireproof high-rises known as skyscrapers.

AUDITORIUM
BUILDING
P42

WAINWRIGHT
BUILDING
P48

MONADNOCK
BUILDING
P54

RELIANCE
BUILDING
P60

FLATIRON
BUILDING
P66

Economic growth in the US was also fuelling the construction industry, and city populations were growing rapidly. Nowhere is this more true than New York. Incredibly, New York's population had tripled between 1840 and 1870, and land prices were at an all-time high by the end of the century. To turn a profit developers had no choice but to create buildings with as many floors as possible, filling them with offices and retail space with the aim of maximising the land's potential. It was only after 1892, however, that the height of buildings in New York could compete with those of Chicago, as until then building codes stated that masonry had to be used as the primary structure for fire prevention. Unlike temples and churches of yesteryear, a building's height was now not only about superiority, but also due to necessity.

The skyscraper boom taking place in the US came to a halt after the Wall Street Crash of 1929, and the following Great Depression. Construction slowed across the board as property prices fell sharply, with many high-rises standing mostly empty, their developers unable to find enough tenants. With a few exceptions, skyscrapers would make their US comeback when the economy picked up in the 1950s, post World War II.

EMPIRE
STATE
BUILDING
P84

CHRYSLER
BUILDING
P78

WOOLWORTH
BUILDING
P72

CONSTRUCTION:
1887–9

HEIGHT:
72.6 M

CHICAGO
USA

AUDITORIUM BUILDING

The Auditorium Building was initially the concept of Ferdinand Peck, a wealthy businessman and philanthropist, who wanted to bring the arts to the people of Chicago by means of a theatre. His vision was for it to be the largest, grandest and most expensive – yet accessible to everyone, from all incomes. So this could be achieved, he decided to include business offices and a luxury hotel, the proceeds of which would go towards subsidising the cost of the theatre tickets. Peck sought the services of architects Dankmar Adler and Louis Sullivan, who set about realising his idea.

The building had prestigious beginnings: the first stone was laid on 5 October 1887 by President Cleveland, and two years later his successor, President Harrison, dedicated the building. On completion it became the tallest building in the city, and the largest in the country, and was praised for its design. Sullivan and Adler had excelled in bringing an aesthetic harmony to the various sections of the building, for at the time it was fairly novel for buildings to be multi-purpose. Despite its immense size, the shape and form of the building wouldn't necessarily make it a skyscraper by today's standards, but the lessons learned from constructing such a building did help influence things to come.

Unfortunately, the hotel and offices could not financially support the theatre, and over the decades it fell into disrepair. In 1941, the Auditorium Theatre went bankrupt and closed, at which point the City of Chicago took it over. Thankfully, due to fundraising campaigns, the theatre reopened in 1967 and remains in operation to this day.

MULTI-PURPOSE

The Auditorium Building was one of the most complex multi-use buildings in the country at this point, and could boast of some impressive statistics. The seventeen-storey office block, ten-storey hotel and spacious theatre, though sharing the same building, each had their own entrance to maintain some degree of separation. Adler and Sullivan rented the top two floors of the tower for their architects' offices.

HOTEL ROOMS
400

THEATRE SEATS
4 237

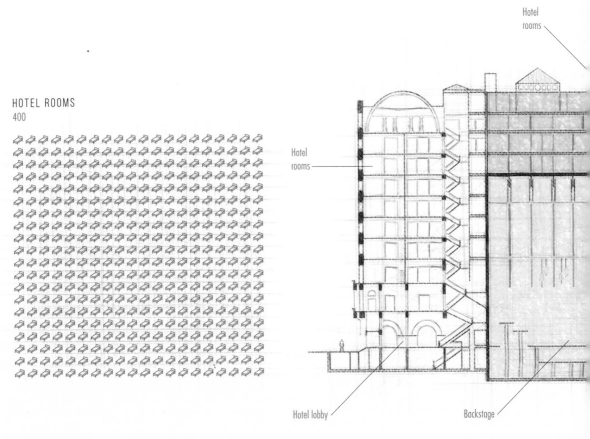

Hotel rooms

Hotel rooms

Hotel lobby

Backstage

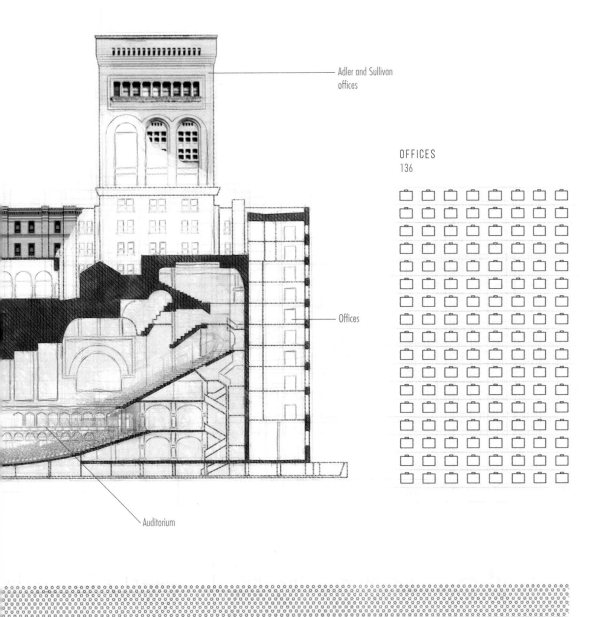

Adler and Sullivan
offices

Offices

Auditorium

OFFICES
136

HEAVYWEIGHT

Not only was the Auditorium Building the tallest in Chicago, but the heaviest as well. The architects opted to use traditional load-bearing masonry walls that greatly contributed to its weight, as the use of steel frames was still in its infancy. The building itself weighs 100 000 tonnes, over four times heavier than the then recently constructed Statue of Liberty (1886), including its pedestal.

72.6 m

93.0 m

24 000 tonnes

100 000 tonnes

FLAT FOUNDATIONS

Chicago sits on soft clay, and without the means to drive foundations deep down to the firm bedrock, a method had to be devised to stop the building from sinking. A system was created that would spread the load of the building to better distribute the pressure. Using railway rails in layers, with each layer running at right angles to the one below, they were built up into a pyramid shape. This structure was set below ground level and caked with concrete, and would prevent the building from sinking or toppling over.

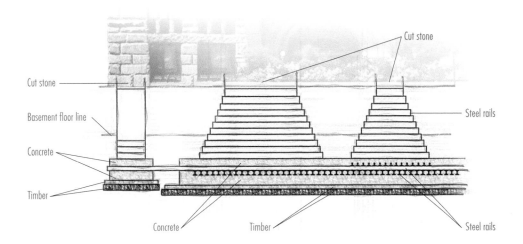

SUBSIDENCE

Despite the best efforts to support the building on the soft ground, the building did subside a little, and dropped about 75 cm over the first ten years before it came to settle. This is noticeable at the ground level where parts of the floor noticeably slope.

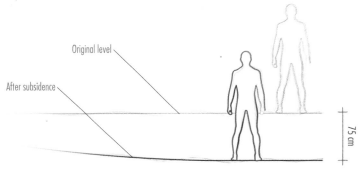

CONSTRUCTION:
1890–1

HEIGHT:
44.8 M

ST LOUIS
USA

WAINWRIGHT BUILDING

The Wainwright Building, like the Auditorium Building, was also a work of Adler and Sullivan, and another milestone in the evolution of the skyscraper. Although the Wainwright doesn't hold the distinction of being the first skyscraper (this title is usually credited to the Home Insurance Building, demolished in 1931), it is often regarded as the first tall building to truly embrace its height. Earlier attempts at constructing tall buildings would often play down their height. Many resorted to unsuitable historical styles, and featured prominent horizontal bands that segregated the building into several sections that seemed to be stacked one on top of the other. The bulk of the Wainwright, by contrast, is distinguished by vertical piers that extend unbroken for most of its height, as though it has seemingly been stretched upwards.

The architects were commissioned by the president of the St Louis Brewing Company, Ellis Wainwright, from whom the building gets its name. He required office space to manage his business, and had a plot of land in the city on which to build. After the success of the Auditorium Building, Adler and Sullivan had made quite a reputation for themselves, prompting Wainwright to seek out their skills. Pleased with their designs he gave the go-ahead for what was to be St Louis' first steel frame building, which would become renowned as one of the earliest true skyscrapers in the world. Construction began in 1890 and was completed the following year.

Wainwright
State Office Building

FORM FOLLOWS FUNCTION

Sullivan's favourite dictum was 'form follows function', by which he meant that the exterior of a building should reflect its interior structure. In the case of high-rise buildings with vertical steel supports such as this, his architectural ethos would serve to make the building look elongated, accentuating its height. By making sure that the windows were recessed from the brick-clad pillars, Sullivan helped to diminish the effects of any horizontal elements. The tripartite nature of the Wainwright also lends itself to the functionality of the building: the lower two floors are accessible to the public, the offices lie in the section with the vertical piers, and the top floor, markedly different, is surrounded by intertwined leaf scrolls framing circular windows, hiding the maintenance equipment.

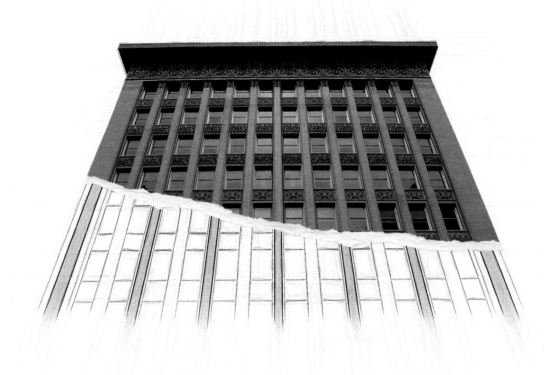

Sullivan's 'form follows function' ethos hasn't fully been adhered to in the case of the Wainwright Building. The exterior of the building might lead one to think that behind each vertical pier there is a structural element, when in fact steel supports are situated at the corners, and only behind every other pier.

TRIPARTITE CONSTRUCTION

Adler and Sullivan's creation was tripartite or, in other words, made from three parts, much in the same way a classical column has a base, a shaft and a top section, known as the *capital*.

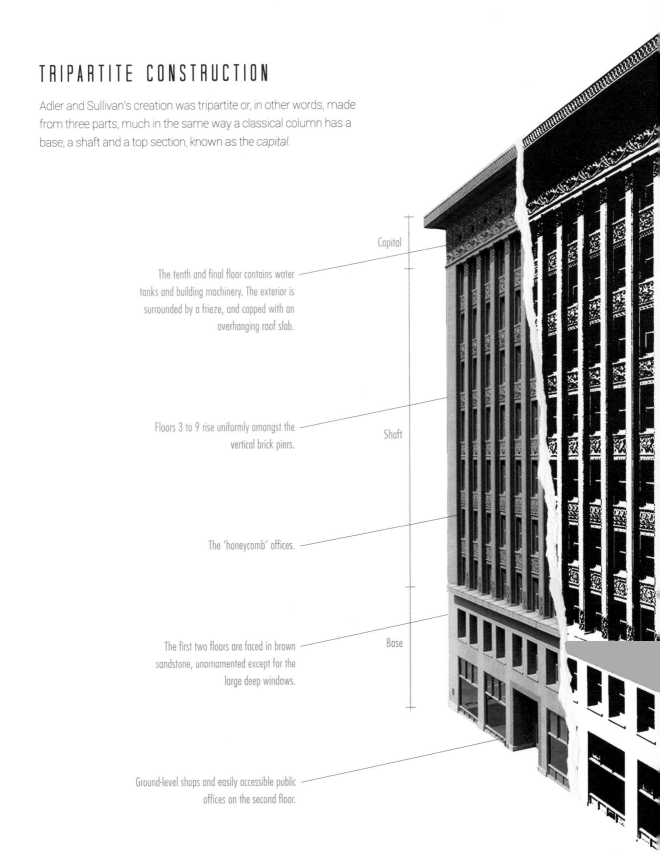

Capital

The tenth and final floor contains water tanks and building machinery. The exterior is surrounded by a frieze, and capped with an overhanging roof slab.

Shaft

Floors 3 to 9 rise uniformly amongst the vertical brick piers.

The 'honeycomb' offices.

Base

The first two floors are faced in brown sandstone, unornamented except for the large deep windows.

Ground-level shops and easily accessible public offices on the second floor.

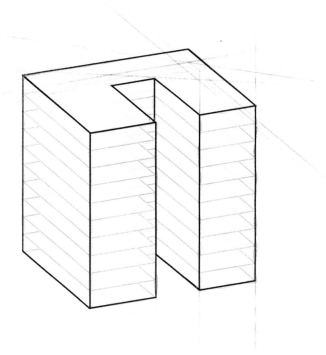

WELL LIT

From the street on to which it faces, and from where it is usually seen, the Wainwright Building appears to be a large, solid block. The building is in fact U-shaped, and surrounds a courtyard. The courtyard allows for the interior to receive more light than would be possible if it was one dense cube, and is known as a 'light court'.

REAR OF BUILDING   BUILDING PLAN

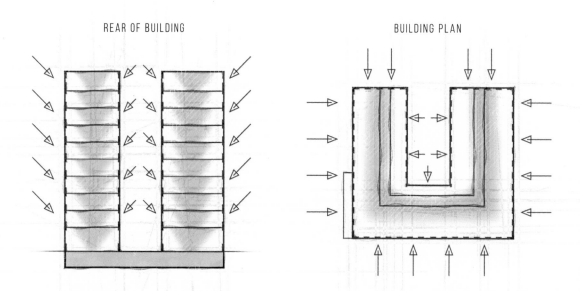

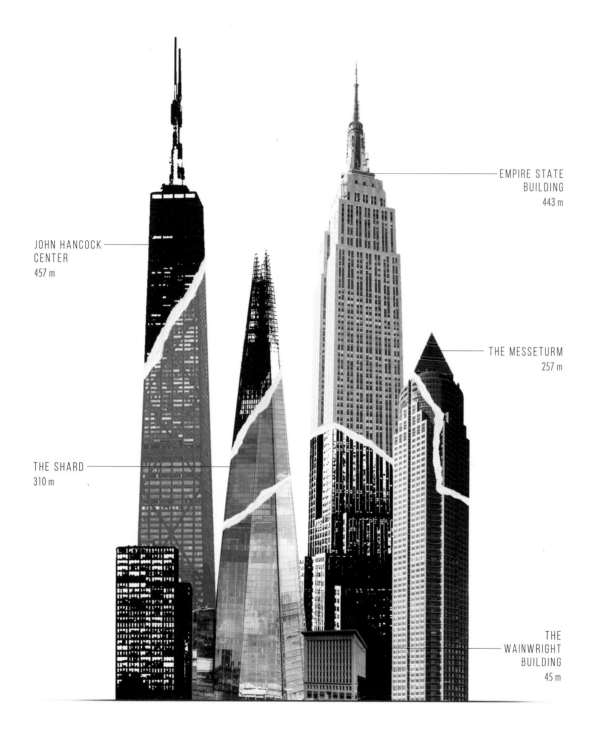

JOHN HANCOCK
CENTER
457 m

EMPIRE STATE
BUILDING
443 m

THE MESSETURM
257 m

THE SHARD
310 m

THE
WAINWRIGHT
BUILDING
45 m

FORERUNNER

Although modern skyscrapers dwarf this ten-storey building,
it's important to remember that everything has a beginning.

CONSTRUCTION:
1891–3

HEIGHT:
60.1m

CHICAGO
USA

MONADNOCK BUILDING

The Monadnock Building is a curious example that sits on the cusp of two architectural eras. Using hefty load-bearing walls, it could be thought of as looking to the past; indeed it has been said that it is 'the last of the big masonry towers'. However, with respect to its use of steel, and as the largest office block in the world when completed, it certainly looked to the future.

After the Great Chicago Fire destroyed 5 km² of the city in 1871, real-estate developer Peter Brooks bought up strategic plots of land, one of which was a fairly narrow (21 m by 61 m) site. He commissioned Burnham & Root, one of the most famous architectural companies of 19th-century Chicago, to design him an office block. He stipulated that it should have clean lines and no protruding surfaces, so as not to accumulate dirt, and that functionality should be at its core. This idea was largely carried through to the final design, although Brooks, on advice, allowed for bay windows to be implemented, as they would maximise the rentable space. The only other hint of ornamentation on the building

would come from the slight flaring at the top. A minimalist approach to tall buildings was forward thinking for the time, hinting at what facades would look like decades later. The permit for the seventeen-storey building was granted in 1889 and construction was completed in 1891.

The building was such a success that Shepherd Brooks, Peter's brother, bought the adjoining plot of land. His intentions were to extend the Monadnock to the south but, by using different architects, and due to keeping costs down, the southern end of the building is quite different. Completed in 1893, it relied more heavily on steel frames to support the load, though the outer appearance is more traditional with neoclassical influences.

Brick wall: 0.45 m

WHERE BRICK REACHED ITS LIMIT

Due to the mass of construction materials they have to support, the walls at ground level are especially thick. They couldn't make the building any higher because the rentable area of the lower floors would have been reduced too drastically. The thickness of the walls reduces as the height of the building increases, as higher levels have much less force acting on them.

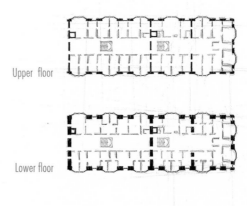

Upper floor

Lower floor

BEYOND THE BOUNDARY

The Monadnock Building used similar foundations to the Auditorium Building, ones that function by distributing the weight of the building over a larger area. In this case we can see that the Monadnock's foundations extend well beyond the building's lot, and out below the street next to it.

Brick wall: 1.80 m

Ground level

Steel rail and concrete lattice

Basement level

3.4 m

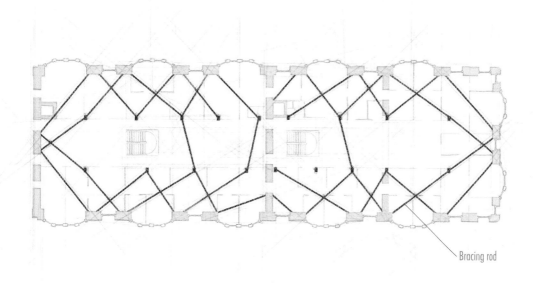

Bracing rod

WIND BRACING

Because of problems inherent with cast iron, tight connections cannot be made with the material, and buildings that use it rely on their thick masonry walls to prevent them from swaying in the wind. The Monadnock came at a time when huge advances had been made in steel production, and so steel was incorporated into the design. By using steel, they were able to create precisely fitted braces that ran diagonally between various struts, providing extra strength where compressive forces would have caused iron to buckle.

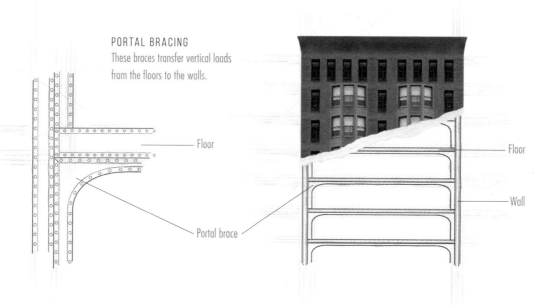

PORTAL BRACING
These braces transfer vertical loads from the floors to the walls.

Floor

Portal brace

Floor

Wall

A BUILDING OF TWO HALVES

Root, one of the lead architects on the north half of the
building, died unexpectedly before he could see his project
completed. The architects Holabird & Roche were brought
in to design the south half, effectively doubling its size. The
buildings were constructed so that they shared a basement
and were connected on every floor, except the 17th floor, the
southern end of which was rentable but the northern end
was attic space.

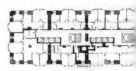

NORTH BUILDING

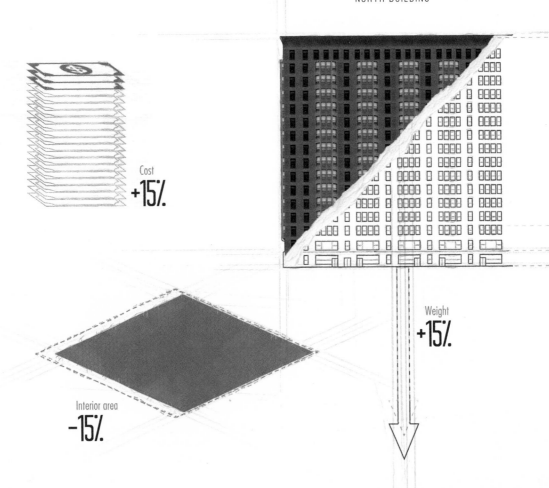

Cost
+15%

Weight
+15%

Interior area
−15%

15 PER CENT

As the south half of the Monadnock relied more on its steel framework to support it, much less stone was needed in its creation, which had a tremendous impact all round. It cost 15 per cent less, weighed 15 per cent less, and offered 15 per cent more rentable space.

SOUTH BUILDING

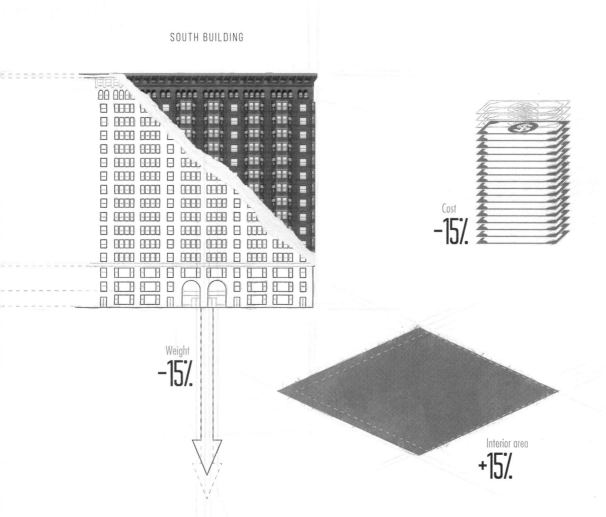

Cost
-15%

Weight
-15%

Interior area
+15%

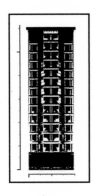

CONSTRUCTION:
1890–5

HEIGHT:
61.5 M

CHICAGO
USA

RELIANCE BUILDING

The Reliance Building is best known for being the first skyscraper to use glass for the majority of its facade. At the time it was quite unique, but this feature would go on to become the prevalent look of tall buildings in the 20th century.

As with the Monadnock building, the Reliance Building was the result of the real-estate boom that happened in Chicago after the Great Fire. A man named William Hale who was, rather appropriately, in the elevator business, bought up a plot of land with the vision of erecting a new tower there. The issue, however, was that on the site there was already a four-storey office block – and not all the tenants wanted to move. Unfettered, Hale progressed anyway. So, in 1890, he had Root (of Burnham & Root) design the first floor and basement while the remaining tenants resided on the second, third and fourth floors. Then, quite unbelievably, he supported the inhabited floors on screw jacks and demolished the ground floor. Work would be carried out on the building's foundations with the tenants suspended above! By 1894 the leases on the upper floors expired, and work on the building resumed. The remaining fourteen floors were finished the following year, although now using the designs of Charles Atwood, due to the untimely death of Root.

The large windows were key to the design of the building, allowing lots of natural light into the offices. This was particularly important for the doctors' rooms, which would be leased higher up the building, as they required good lighting for their examinations. The white terracotta the building is faced with also helped to project an image of hygiene and cleanliness to their patients. It was assumed that the glazed terracotta would never need cleaning, that it was so smooth that rain would wash the dirt away. Unfortunately these assumptions were unfounded.

CURTAIN WALL

Unlike the Monadnock before it, the Reliance Building's external walls would provide no lateral support. Instead, the interlocking exterior walls were attached to the outside of the steel structure, supporting their own weight, but none of the building's. This type of wall is known as a curtain wall, and had been used before but never on such a large scale. Oriel Chambers (1864) in Liverpool, England, features the world's first metal-framed glass curtain wall, but it is far smaller – only five storeys high with no elevator.

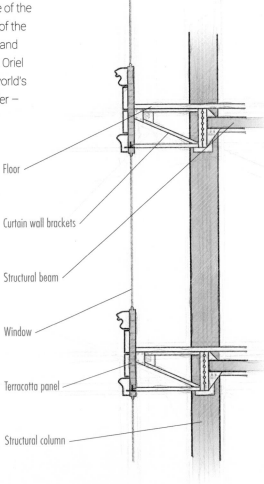

RELIANCE BUILDING
CURTAIN WALL

Floor

Curtain wall brackets

Structural beam

Window

Terracotta panel

Structural column

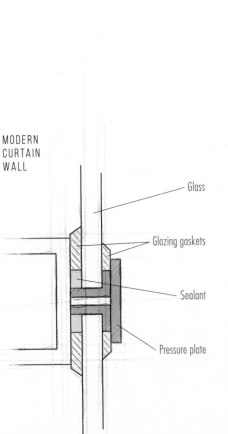

MODERN
CURTAIN
WALL

Glass

Glazing gaskets

Sealant

Pressure plate

On the Reliance Building, glass is set neatly into the thin terracotta panels of the curtain walls to allow light into the building. Over the years, and with the advancement of technology, different styles of curtain walls have emerged. On many modern buildings no masonry or steel framework is visible from the exterior, as more advanced fittings mean the panes of glass seamlessly fit together.

CHICAGO WINDOWS

CHICAGO WINDOWS

The buildings that were springing up in Chicago towards the turn of the 20th century became known as belonging to the 'Chicago School' of architecture. One feature that is synonymous with the Chicago School is the 'Chicago window', which features prominently on the Reliance Building. The Chicago window is comprised of a large fixed central pane of glass and slim, openable windows running down either side. They are typically laid out in grid fashion and, as with the Reliance, columns of windows are sometimes extruded to form bay windows, a design which is both adept at ventilating the interior and filling it with light.

RELIANCE BUILDING'S BAY WINDOWS

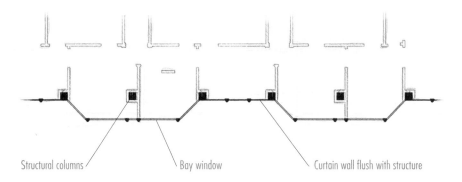

Structural columns   Bay window   Curtain wall flush with structure

MORE WINDOW THAN WALL

As the first skyscraper to use more glass than any other material on its facade, it was definitely a forerunner of things to come. Here you can see the ratio of glass to ceramic on the Reliance Building's exterior.

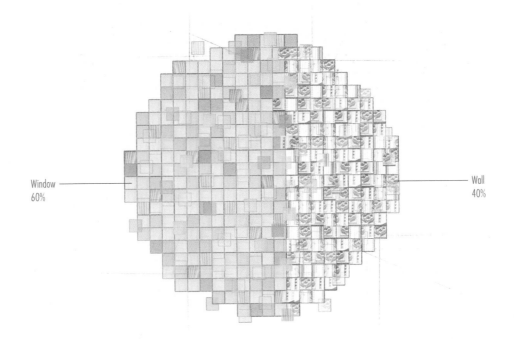

Window
60%

Wall
40%

STEEL BEATS STONE

After the final tenants moved out, the remaining fourteen stories of the building could be built. The steel structure was completed in just twelve weeks, a rate that would have been utterly unthinkable had they been made of conventional masonry.

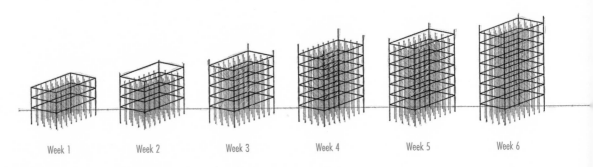

| Week 1 | Week 2 | Week 3 | Week 4 | Week 5 | Week 6 |

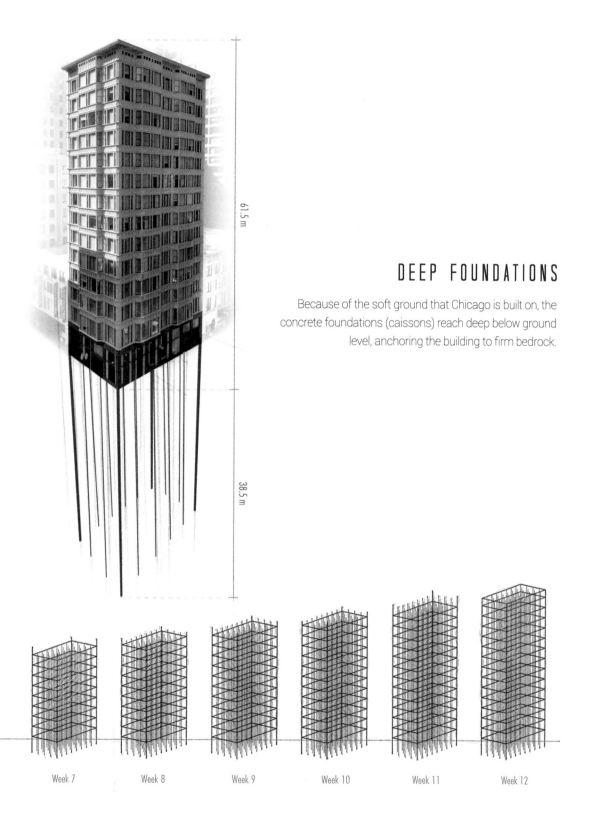

61.5 m

38.5 m

DEEP FOUNDATIONS

Because of the soft ground that Chicago is built on, the concrete foundations (caissons) reach deep below ground level, anchoring the building to firm bedrock.

Week 7   Week 8   Week 9   Week 10   Week 11   Week 12

CONSTRUCTION:
1901–2

HEIGHT:
86.9 M

NEW YORK
USA

FLATIRON BUILDING

One of the oldest surviving and most iconic skyscrapers in New York, the distinctive shape of the Flatiron Building is not easily forgotten. Being so tall and slender, and so ahead of its time, New Yorkers began placing bets on when the wind would topple it.

The triangular plot of land was bought up in 1899 by Harry Black of prosperous contractors the Fuller Company to host the site of their new headquarters. On the site stood a seven-storey hotel and some smaller commercial buildings, which would have to be demolished. Black saw that the site's potential wasn't being reached, especially now that construction laws had been loosened to allow for steel-framed buildings, and the booming New York population would only ever drive up prices. He brought on board architect Daniel Burnham, who at the time was famed for his work in Chicago, to draw up plans for the unusual plot of land.

Several designs were drawn up, with Black pushing hard for the inclusion of a retail space on the ground floor that would increase revenue. Burnham, again using the tripartite design that had been developed in Chicago, opposed this idea. He felt that it interrupted the sense of symmetry that he had developed between the top and bottom of the building, but Black insisted on it.

Upon its completion in 1902 the twenty-storey building was the tallest office building in the world. It holds the distinction of being the world's first free-standing skyscraper, as all previous tall buildings had either been large palazzo-style structures, or shared at least one wall with neighbouring buildings. Three years after completion, another floor would be added, taking it to twenty-one storeys above ground and the height that it is today.

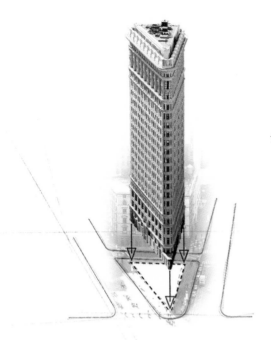

THE FLATIRON LAND

The plot of land was known by locals as The Flatiron before the building itself was constructed. The building was originally called the Fuller Building after George A. Fuller, founder of the Fuller Company, but, as people persisted in calling it The Flatiron, the name was officially changed.

DIFFERENT ANGLES

Due to its unconventional shape, the building's appearance changes dramatically depending on the angle it is viewed from.

INTERNAL PECULIARITIES

Due to an oversight in design, there was only one set of toilets per floor, meaning that designated men's and women's toilets were on alternating floors. Also, to get to the top floor you must take an elevator to the 20th, then take another to the 21st. This is due to the last floor being added at a later date.

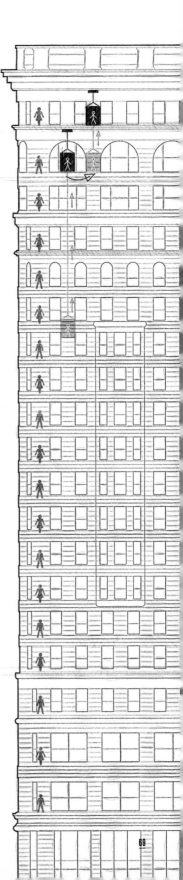

FACADE

Although the building was constructed in a classical tripartite fashion much like the Wainwright Building, it features a lot more decoration than other high-rises at the turn of the century. The terracotta ornamental panelling includes flowers, wreathes and Medusa heads inspired by the French and Italian Renaissance periods.

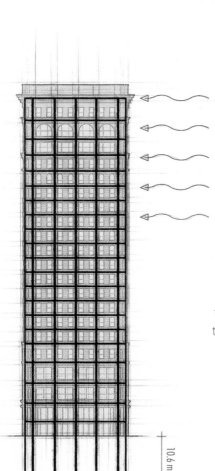

10.6 m

STRONGER THAN EXPECTED

Despite people's lack of confidence in the new building, and their doubts about its relatively shallow foundations, it has never toppled. The steel bracing was designed to withstand four times the amount of wind force than it would ever be exposed to.

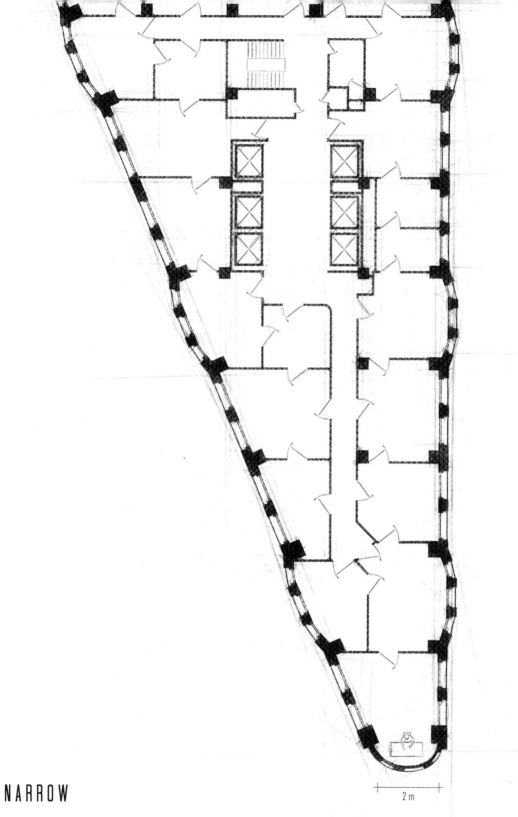

NARROW

At its tip the Flatiron Building is only 2 m wide.

2 m

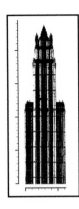

CONSTRUCTION:
1910-3

HEIGHT:
241.4 M

NEW YORK
USA

WOOLWORTH BUILDING

Shortly after the turn of the 20th century, skyscrapers began springing up throughout New York, fuelled by ambitious entrepreneurs and ingenious architects. For many, these buildings of the future were awe-inspiring, but others were concerned that the changes they would bring would not be for the better. Fearing that the streets would one day be plunged into darkness, that the public transport system would become swamped, and that the commercial district would sprawl into surrounding residential areas, city officials began making recommendations to limit the size of new constructs. It was against this backdrop that the Woolworth Building came to be.

Frank Woolworth, founder of the company that bears his name, commissioned architect Cass Gilbert to design the company's new headquarters. Originally, the plans were for it to be 130 m tall, although these were swiftly reworked into plans for a colossal 241 m building as no legislation had yet been passed. Having paid the total cost himself without any need for investors, Woolworth had an unusual amount of freedom with its design and development. Indeed, the choice to implement Neo-Gothic architecture was partly inspired by his vision of himself as a descendant of the great medieval merchants of the past. The choice of style also seemed to be an effort to placate those who thought that the new bombardment of modern skyscrapers would detract from the more historic elements of the city.

In 1913 the world's tallest building was opened, with President Woodrow Wilson turning on the floodlights by pressing a button in Washington DC, a novel innovation for the time. Also at the ceremony, Reverend C. Parkes Cadman referred to the building as the 'Cathedral of Commerce', bestowing upon it its most applicable nickname.

STRENGTH AND FOUNDATIONS

The steel frame's design was dictated by the wind loads it would be exerted to: K-shaped knee braces are used high up the tower, steel arches, known as portal braces, rigidly connect columns on the middle floors, and concentric chevron bracing reinforces the base of the tower.

FOUNDATION PLAN

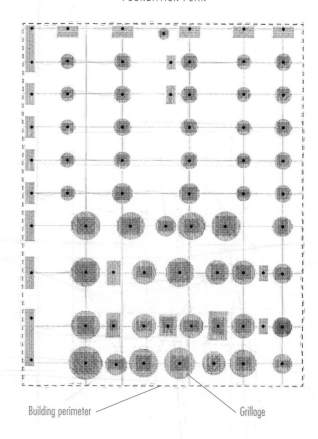

Building perimeter

Grillage

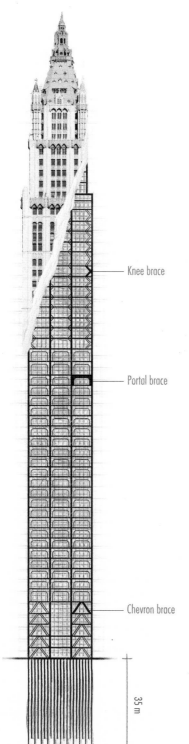

Knee brace

Portal brace

Chevron brace

35 m

To anchor the building down, sixty-nine caissons were driven into the bedrock. A 'grillage' of crisscrossing steel beams was positioned at the top of each one to also spread the massive loads.

GOTHIC DECORATION

Although freestanding like the Flatiron Building, the Woolworth Building's aesthetic is Gothic rather than classical. In many ways this seems to be a more appropriate choice; because the Gothic style evolved from the construction of medieval churches and towering cathedrals, it is a more 'vertical' style of architecture.

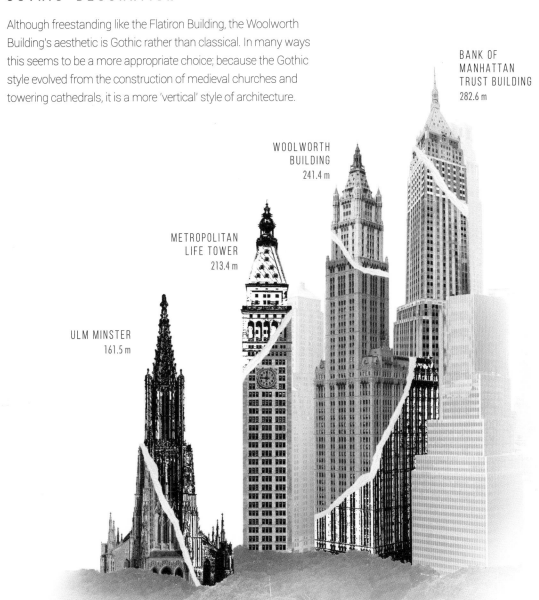

BANK OF
MANHATTAN
TRUST BUILDING
282.6 m

WOOLWORTH
BUILDING
241.4 m

METROPOLITAN
LIFE TOWER
213.4 m

ULM MINSTER
161.5 m

WORLD'S TALLEST BUILDING

Upon construction it surpassed the Metropolitan Life Tower to become the world's tallest building, holding the title for seventeen years. It was beaten in 1930, by the Bank of Manhattan Trust Building.

GROSS FLOOR AREA

Upon its completion the Woolworth Building contained more floor space than any other office building in the world. Today, that title is held by the Pentagon.

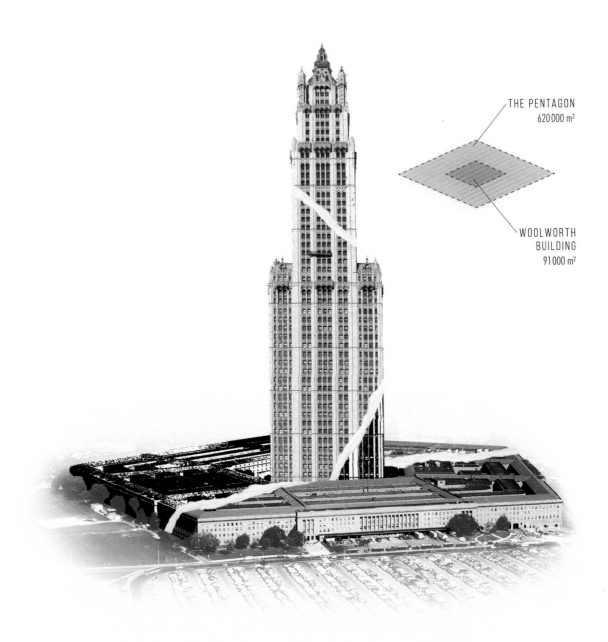

THE PENTAGON
620 000 m²

WOOLWORTH
BUILDING
91 000 m²

TAPERED SHAFTS

The elevator shafts were tapered slightly, getting narrower towards the bottom. This had the effect that, should the lift go into free-fall, air pressure would build under the car, and this cushion of air would prevent the lift from gathering too much speed. It is said that this was tested with empty cars before the building opened.

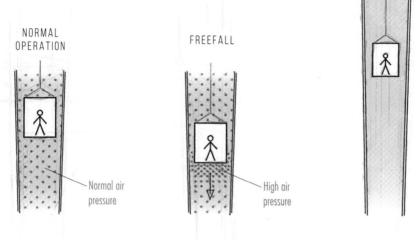

NORMAL OPERATION

FREEFALL

Normal air pressure

High air pressure

HIGH-TECH ELEVATORS

New, high-speed electric elevators were installed in the Woolworth Building, without which the building may not have been possible. Most elevators of the time were still hydraulically powered, and were much less efficient. The lifts were capable of 12.8 km per hour, similar to many lifts today.

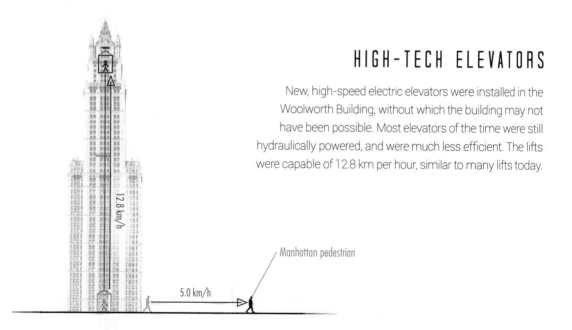

12.8 km/h

Manhattan pedestrian

5.0 km/h

CONSTRUCTION:
1928–30

HEIGHT:
319.0 M

NEW YORK
USA

CHRYSLER BUILDING

The Chrysler Building is one of the most iconic skyscrapers in New York, a classic example of the grandeur of art deco architecture in the automobile age. Commerce was booming in New York at the time, and advances in construction technology were occurring rapidly, fuelling a race to build ever higher.

Had things gone to plan, automobile magnate Walter P. Chrysler, founder of the Chrysler Corporation, may never have got his hands on the property. The site was owned by developer William H. Reynolds who, along with architect William Van Allen, had plans for a 206 m tower close to Grand Central Terminal. Reynolds, however, ran out of money, and Chrysler stepped in, buying the land and the project in October 1928.

Chrysler continued to work with Van Allen, asking him to redesign his current plans to add extra storeys, bringing the height to 282 m. Van Allen was eager to accept the challenge, not only because of the prestige, but because he would be competing for vertical superiority with the Manhattan Company Building, which was being constructed simultaneously. This was of particular personal importance to Van Allen, as the Manhattan Company Building's designer was also his former business partner, H. Craig Severance, with whom he'd recently had a bitter parting of ways.

The redesigns that Chrysler asked for would also see the building's aesthetic altered to incorporate visual elements from Chrysler automobiles. He requested a lavish

office and apartment suite at the top too, specifically requesting that the builders made sure his toilet was the highest in Manhattan, so that he could 'shit on Henry Ford and the rest of the world'. It was, in his mind's eye, a monument to himself.

The Chrysler building was completed in 1930 and with some last-minute adjustments beat the competition to reign above all others, if not for very long. Although it would serve as the company headquarters from 1930 until the mid 1950s, it never belonged to the company. Chrysler financed the entire project out of his own money, so that his sons could one day inherit the property.

SECRET SPIRE

While under construction, the Bank of Manhattan Trust Building (now known as 40 Wall Street) had already changed its plans to lengthen its spire. By doing so it would stand a total of 26 m higher than the planned Chrysler.

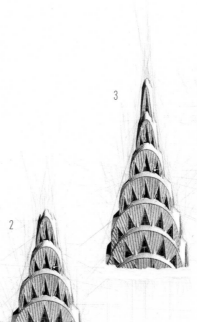

Not to be outdone, Van Allen and Chrysler obtained permission for a 56 m spire, replacing the domed roof that was originally intended. The spire was constructed in secret inside the building, and on 23 October 1929, to everyone's amazement, it was raised into place. The four sections took just ninety minutes to rivet together, dashing the competition's hopes at the final stages.

CONSTRUCTION SPEED

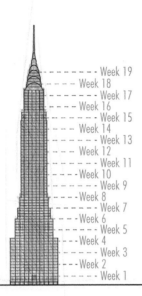

Week 19
Week 18
Week 17
Week 16
Week 15
Week 14
Week 13
Week 12
Week 11
Week 10
Week 9
Week 8
Week 7
Week 6
Week 5
Week 4
Week 3
Week 2
Week 1

By the end of January 1929 the foundations had been excavated and construction on the site started in haste. The first steel beams were set in place at the end of March, and in the spirit of the times, work was undertaken at an astounding rate. The steel framework was completed by September the same year, rising on average four floors a week. Unusually for the time, there were no fatal accidents in the construction of the steelwork, a fact that Chrysler was particularly proud of.

MANPOWER

To maintain the speed at which these giant buildings were constructed, the materials and workforce needed careful organisation so as not to fall behind. At its peak there were 3000 people working on site at the Chrysler Building.

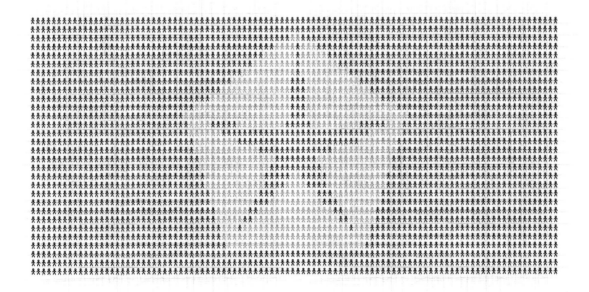

319 m

300 m

WORLD'S TALLEST STRUCTURE

On completion, the Chrysler Building had not only surpassed the Bank of Manhattan Trust Building as the tallest building in the world, but also the Eiffel Tower as the tallest structure, if only by 18 m. The Eiffel Tower held the record for a notable forty-two years, whereas the Chrysler Building held the title for only eleven months, when it was overtaken by the Empire State Building. One prize that can't be taken away from the Chrysler, however, is that it is the first human construct to pass 1 000 feet (305 m) in height, and to this day it retains the title of the tallest steel-supported brick building.

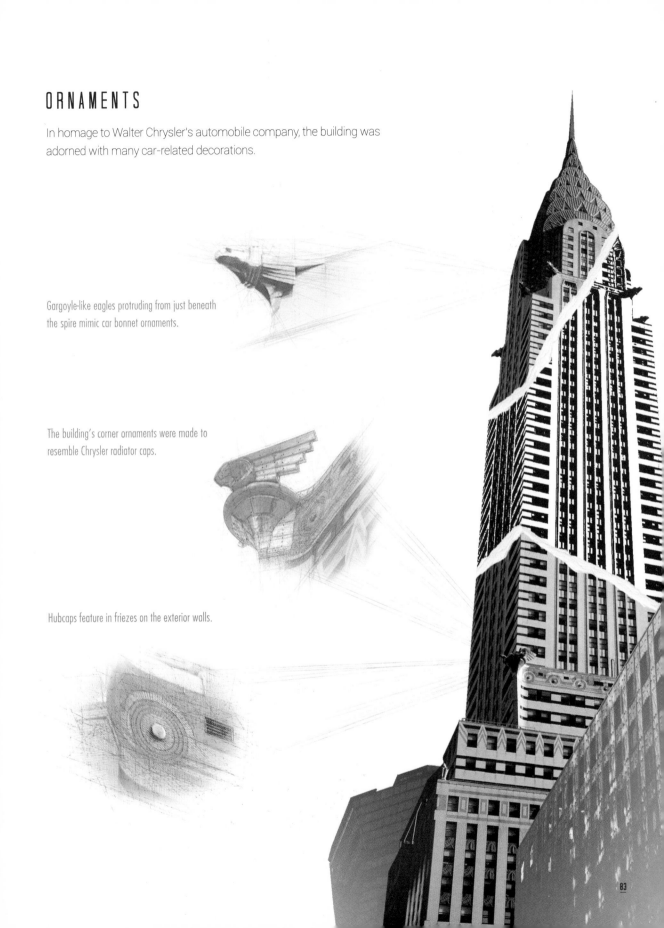

ORNAMENTS

In homage to Walter Chrysler's automobile company, the building was adorned with many car-related decorations.

Gargoyle-like eagles protruding from just beneath the spire mimic car bonnet ornaments.

The building's corner ornaments were made to resemble Chrysler radiator caps.

Hubcaps feature in friezes on the exterior walls.

CONSTRUCTION:
1930–1

HEIGHT:
443.2 м

NEW YORK
USA

EMPIRE STATE BUILDING

The Empire State Building represents the pinnacle of architectural achievement before the Great Depression took hold of the US. Rising nearly half a kilometre into the sky, it soared past its contenders on the New York skyline to become the tallest building in the world – a title it held for almost forty years.

By the 1920s, the plot of land, which contained the original Waldorf Astoria hotel, was bought up by a business venture named Empire State Inc. Amongst the investors was John J. Raskob, who is credited with approaching architect William F. Lamb with the idea for the building. As the story goes, Raskob, in conversation with Lamb, was toying with a jumbo pencil. He stood it on end and said to Lamb, 'Bill, how high can you make it so that it won't fall down?' and thus the idea behind the Empire State Building was born. Plans were drawn up quickly – Lamb had based the drawings on the Reynolds Building (a project his firm had just finished working on) and they were submitted in just two weeks. Raskob liked the designs, but had them revised, then revised again, and again, each time adding

more floors, and more height, until they were well beyond the reaches of their fiercest competitor – the Chrysler Building. Indeed, Raskob, after seeing the trick manoeuvre that the Chrysler had pulled with its spire, wanted to gain a safe lead in case they tried to do it again. Once the final plans were approved, building commenced rapidly; excavation of the site began in January 1930, and the steel frame rose at an incredible rate. It was structurally complete on 11 April 1931, ahead of schedule and under budget.

Due to the Great Depression it would be a long time before anyone had the means to outdo the Empire State Building. It was actually because of the economic downturn that the building was constructed below the expected costs. As the markets had collapsed after the project began, wages were at an all-time low, which worked out well in the short term. Unfortunately, though, because of the financial situation, the building was hard to fill and didn't start making a profit until the 1950s.

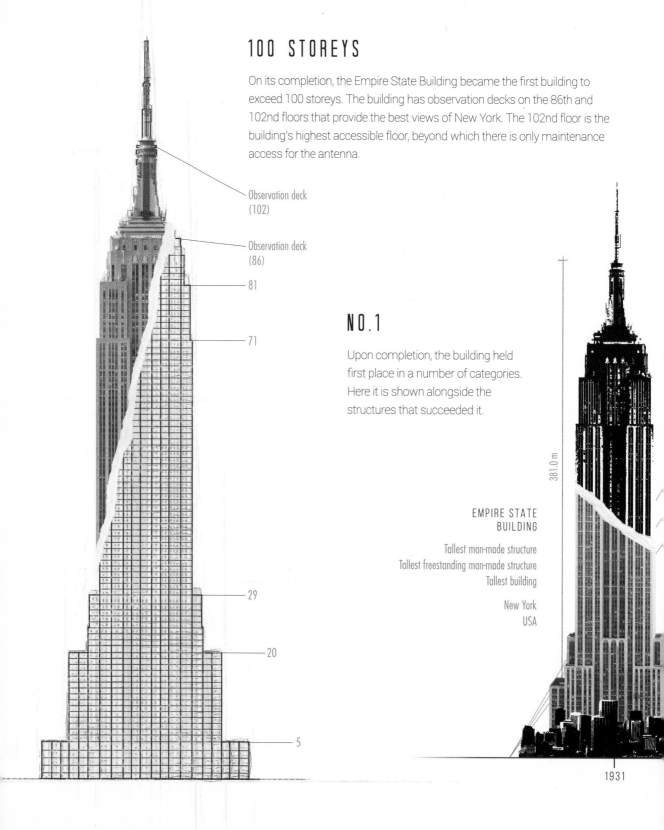

100 STOREYS

On its completion, the Empire State Building became the first building to exceed 100 storeys. The building has observation decks on the 86th and 102nd floors that provide the best views of New York. The 102nd floor is the building's highest accessible floor, beyond which there is only maintenance access for the antenna.

Observation deck (102)

Observation deck (86)

81

71

NO.1

Upon completion, the building held first place in a number of categories. Here it is shown alongside the structures that succeeded it.

29

20

EMPIRE STATE BUILDING

Tallest man-made structure
Tallest freestanding man-made structure
Tallest building

New York
USA

381.0 m

5

1931

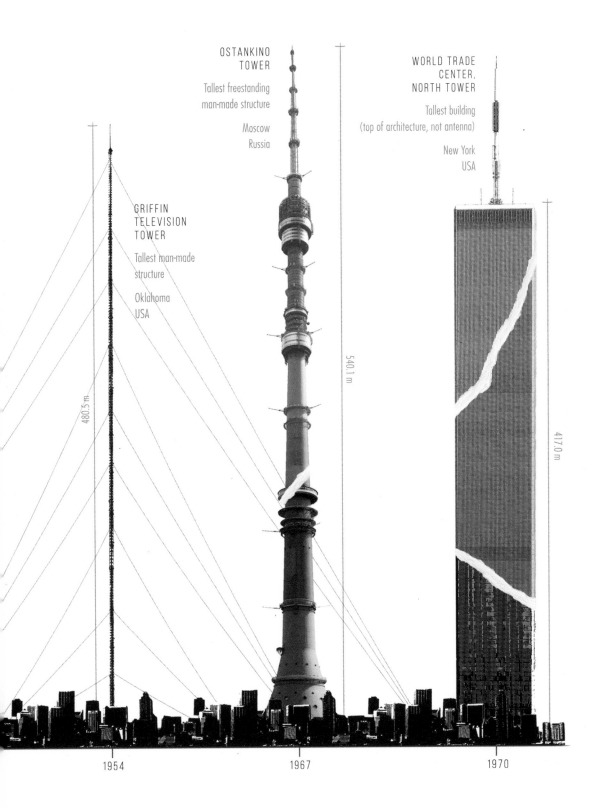

OSTANKINO
TOWER

Tallest freestanding
man-made structure

Moscow
Russia

GRIFFIN
TELEVISION
TOWER

Tallest man-made
structure

Oklahoma
USA

WORLD TRADE
CENTER,
NORTH TOWER

Tallest building
(top of architecture, not antenna)

New York
USA

480.5 m

540.1 m

417.0 m

1954

1967

1970

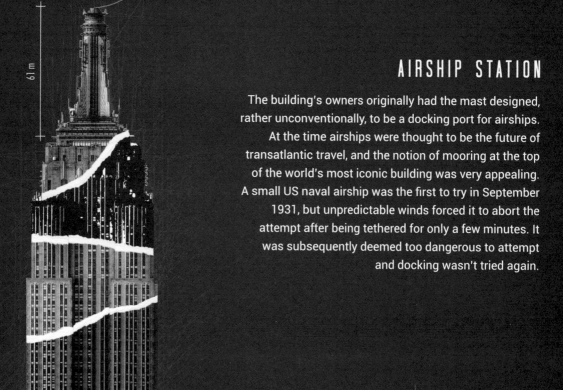

61 m

AIRSHIP STATION

The building's owners originally had the mast designed, rather unconventionally, to be a docking port for airships. At the time airships were thought to be the future of transatlantic travel, and the notion of mooring at the top of the world's most iconic building was very appealing. A small US naval airship was the first to try in September 1931, but unpredictable winds forced it to abort the attempt after being tethered for only a few minutes. It was subsequently deemed too dangerous to attempt and docking wasn't tried again.

ANTENNA

Shown on the opposite page, the building's roof is as it was when originally constructed, reaching 380 m at the top of the mooring mast. By 1953 the broadcasting antenna was mounted at the summit, taking the structural height to 443 m.

63 m

CHANGING LIGHTS

The building was originally adorned by a single white searchlight on its roof until, in 1956, three more were added. This changed in 1976 when the Empire State Building's rooftop lights became multicoloured, starting the tradition of altering the colour in recognition of various holidays, events and special occasions. The system received an update in 2012 with LEDs that, between them, are able to display 16 million colours and can change instantaneously. Here the red, white and blue are in honour of President's Day.

GOING GLOBAL

Although skyscrapers were popping up at an alarming rate in the US around the turn of the 20th century, the scene elsewhere was quite different. The US was undergoing mass immigration that forced land prices in the cities to skyrocket, so much so that skyscrapers seemed the only sensible option. In other regions of the world during this period this was not the case, at least not to nearly the same degree.

The first high-rise appeared in Europe just before the year 1900, in Rotterdam in the Netherlands. The Witte Huis was a ten-storey office building, created not so much out of necessity, but due to its architects becoming inspired by the tall buildings they had seen on a trip to New York. The building, although it used some iron and steel framework, still relied heavily on masonry and therefore is often overlooked in favour of the Royal Liver Building in Liverpool, which was built in 1911. The Royal Liver Building more closely fits the bill when it comes to materials and construction techniques, yet still did not surpass 100 m in height. Despite European cities clearly not being afraid to build tall, as is proven by the many cathedrals, there was a reticence when it came to the skyscraper. In fact, by 1950 the US had over 200 buildings over 100 m in height, and a handful of others

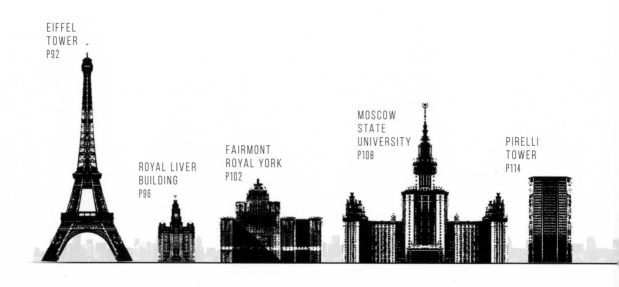

EIFFEL
TOWER
P92

ROYAL LIVER
BUILDING
P96

FAIRMONT
ROYAL YORK
P102

MOSCOW
STATE
UNIVERSITY
P108

PIRELLI
TOWER
P114

had emerged in Canada and South America, and yet Europe only had one. It was only after World War II, when economies started recovering, that Europe began to experiment with tall buildings.

It wasn't until the 1960s, when reinforced concrete had been in use for about fifty years, that another scientific leap would propel skyscrapers into a new age. The arrival of computer technology meant that architects received a vital tool in the advancement of their craft. Computer-aided architectural design (CAAD) would massively streamline the procedure: blueprints would no longer need to be drawn by hand, lengthy and complex calculations could be performed in a fraction of the time, construction materials could be used more sparingly — all of which contributed to fewer man-hours and lower project costs. Coupled with the ever stronger materials that were being developed, structures that would not have been possible a decade ago were now within reach.

By the end of the 20th century, with World War II a distant memory for most, world economies were, on the whole, stronger than ever. High-rises had become a common sight on continents around the globe.

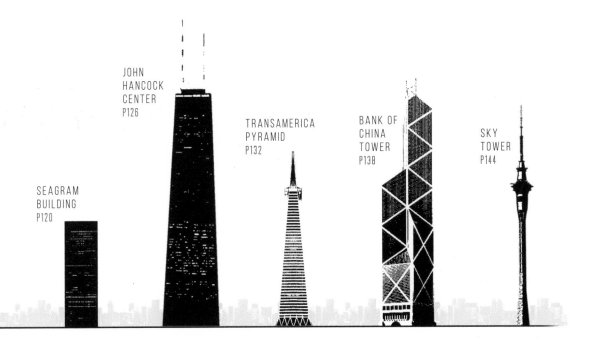

JOHN
HANCOCK
CENTER
P126

TRANSAMERICA
PYRAMID
P132

BANK OF
CHINA
TOWER
P138

SKY
TOWER
P144

SEAGRAM
BUILDING
P120

EIFFEL TOWER

The Eiffel Tower may not be a skyscraper in terms of construct – it has no exterior walls and few floors – but because of its height and its iron structure it is definitely a significant relative. When it was completed it became the tallest man-made structure in the world at 300 m – it would reach its current height in 1957 with the addition of its broadcasting aerials. Originally intended as a temporary exhibit, the Eiffel Tower was saved from being dismantled when city officials realised its usefulness for radio communications.

In 1889, Paris was to host a world's fair to showcase the achievements of various nations. With France being the host nation the government was eager to impress, and in an effort to get the country's brightest minds

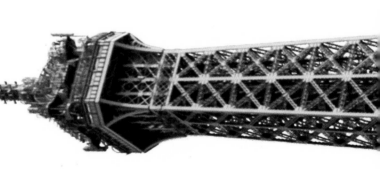

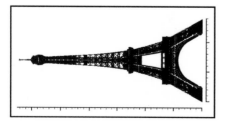

CONSTRUCTION:
1887–89
HEIGHT:
324.0 M
PARIS
FRANCE

retirement the previous year. Xiaoping was the man responsible for China's economic reforms that had opened up their markets to the global economy, and who saw the potential in transforming Shanghai into the financial centre of the nation. Xiaoping urged the city's municipal government to invest in the Pudong district, a largely neglected area of the city. Within months the area was flattened and ready to be transformed.

Chicago firm Skidmore, Owings & Merrill (SOM) were the architects brought on board for the project. One of the largest architectural firms in the world, SOM have offices internationally and have carried out projects in over fifty countries. The company was founded in 1937 and has become primarily renowned for high-end commercial buildings, and has designed many of the world's tallest buildings. In the same vein as the Petronas Towers, the SOM designs were intended to capture the spirit and history of the region, while creating a new-age technical marvel. This they achieved, creating a beautifully proportioned tapered structure clad in a sleek aluminium lattice frame, yet one that is also instantly recognisable as having its roots in China's original skyscraper – the pagoda.

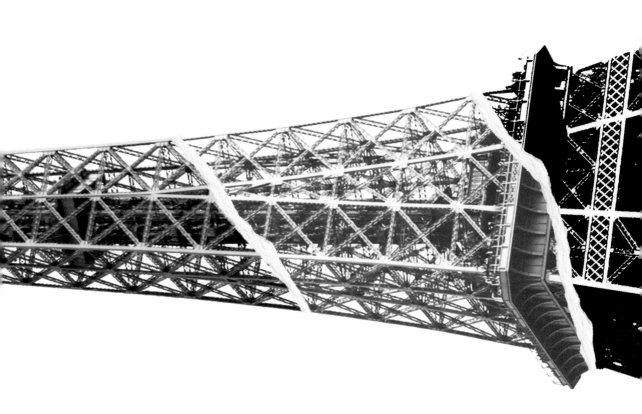

STATUE OF LIBERTY

Gustave Eiffel was greatly respected for his understanding and use of iron. Shortly before turning his attention to the tower that bears his name, he designed and built the internal structure for the Statue of Liberty.

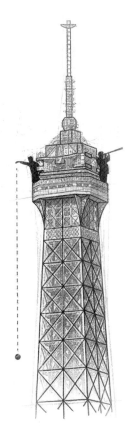

THERMAL EXPANSION

Eiffel had a small office at the top of the tower from which he used to study how air resistance acted on falling bodies. The high vantage point also allowed him to conduct meteorological observations.

PINNACLE OF PARIS

The Eiffel Tower has been the tallest structure in Paris since it came into existence over 200 years ago. The office skyscraper Tour First, completed in 1974, is next in line, but still a way off nonetheless.

324 m

231 m

THERMAL EXPANSION

The Eiffel Tower sways fractionally in the wind, as will any tall building. However, because it is made solely of iron, it is also noticeably effected by the sun – on a hot day the tower can grow by 15 cm. If the sun is low and shining on just one side of the structure then that side will expand more than the other, causing the tower to lean away from the sun by up to 18 cm.

CONSTRUCTION:
1908–11

HEIGHT:
98.2 M

LIVERPOOL
ENGLAND

ROYAL LIVER BUILDING

Liverpool's waterfront is home to a trio of buildings constructed in the early 1900s, the most notable of which is the Royal Liver Building. Often regarded as Britain's first skyscraper, not only because of its height but also its pioneering use of reinforced concrete – a material that the majority of tall buildings use to this day – the building's design is indeed quite comparable to the skyscrapers being built in the US during the same period.

The Royal Liver Building was built to provide office space for the Royal Liver Group, a company founded in 1850 that provided assistance to local people should they lose a wage-earning relative. Their services quickly spread throughout the UK, and by the late 1890s a decision was made to build a large office building for their ever-growing workforce. It wasn't until 1907, however, when their workforce reached 6000, that they selected a site and approved the building's designs. The architect they hired was Walter

Aubrey Thomas, who was experienced in designing commercial buildings, having established his own practice in Liverpool some thirty years earlier. He is particularly noted for his creativity and technological know-how, and at least seven of his buildings are protected by the English Heritage Trust for their historical and architectural significance.

The foundation stone was laid on 11 May 1908, and despite many doubting that it was even possible to build, construction took only three years, and the Royal Liver Building was officially opened on 19 July 1911. Along with its two neighbouring structures, built in the years just before and after, the building is a key component in enhancing the city's maritime gateway. Standing tall at thirteen storeys above ground, it was the tallest building in Britain until the arrival of tower blocks in the 1960s.

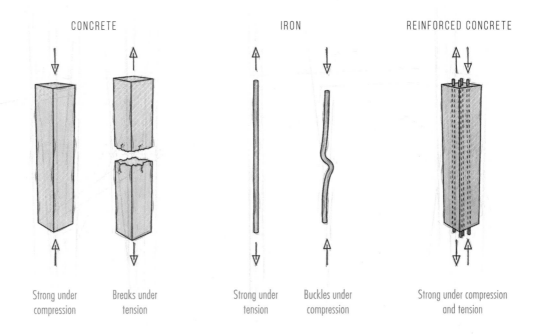

CONCRETE

Strong under
compression

Breaks under
tension

IRON

Strong under
tension

Buckles under
compression

REINFORCED CONCRETE

Strong under compression
and tension

REINFORCED CONCRETE

The Royal Liver Building was the first building of its size in the world to utilise reinforced concrete. Concrete on its own performs well under compressive loads, but poorly under tension. However, by embedding an iron structure into the concrete, any tensile loads will be transmitted through the iron, which performs better under such loads. The system used was developed by French engineer François Hennebique, which he patented in 1892. It was one of the first methods of using reinforced concrete, with which he crafted separate construction components, such as columns and beams, into one monolithic object.

HENNEBIQUE BEAM AND COLUMNS

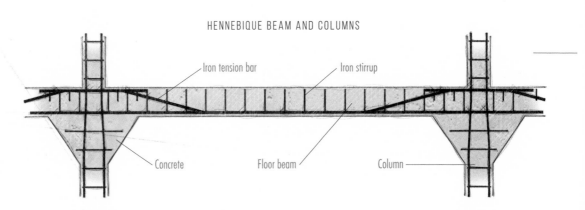

Iron tension bar

Iron stirrup

Concrete

Floor beam

Column

MASSIVE FORCES

Due to the use of reinforced concrete, the various structural elements could withstand huge forces. There are hundreds of horizontal beams that span up to 15 m, and arches that span 18 m that are able to withstand 1 420 tonnes. The columns throughout the building are able to withstand 1525 tonnes. Had the building been made from masonry, the walls would have to have been impossibly thick.

30 m

18 m

625 tonnes

625 tonnes

50-YEAR REIGN

The Royal Liver Building remained the tallest building in Liverpool for over fifty years, when it was overtaken by St John's Beacon in 1965.

RADIO CITY

148.0 m

98.2 m

THREE GRACES

The Royal Liver Building sits adjacent to the Cunard Building (completed in 1917), and just beyond that the Port of Liverpool Building (completed in 1907). Together the buildings are known as the Three Graces.

ROYAL LIVER
BUILDING
1911

CUNARD
BUILDING
1917

BIG TIME

The clock faces on the two towers needed to be large so that passing sailors could easily tell the time; they are actually slightly larger than the ones on Big Ben. They are called George clocks because they were started at the exact time King George V was crowned.

Royal Liver Building

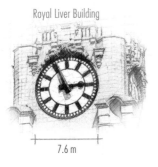

+---- 7.6 m ----+

Big Ben

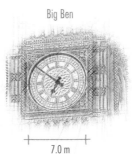

+---- 7.0 m ----+

LIVER BIRDS

Two mythical creatures, known as Liver Birds, stand on top of the towers. Bertie faces the city, looking out for its inhabitants, and Bella faces the other way, out to sea. They are constructed from moulded and hammered copper, and were originally gilded.

+---- 7.3 m ----+

PORT OF
LIVERPOOL
BUILDING
1907

CONSTRUCTION:
1927–9

HEIGHT:
124.0 м

TORONTO
CANADA

FAIRMONT ROYAL YORK

When it was first announced that the Royal York was to be built, it was not met with much enthusiasm from Toronto's inhabitants. On the chosen site there already stood a hotel, the Queen's Hotel, one of the largest and best-equipped hotels in Canada, parts of which dated back to 1844. Understandably, locals weren't keen on losing part of their heritage, however this feeling could only last so long – such a magnificent building as this was certain to win the people over.

After the death of Henry Winnett, the hotelier and owner of the Queen's Hotel, in 1925, his estate sold the property to the Canadian Pacific Railway. The site was ideally suited to a hotel as it was within close proximity to two railway stations, and Canadian Pacific knew that with their backing the site had more potential. It would be more than just a hotel, more than just an opulent destination, it would be the sort of building that a thriving city needs to put itself on the map. The variety of functions the building serves is common in most present-day large buildings, but was still quite novel for the time, adding to the sense of modernity and luxury.

Upon its completion, the Royal York became the tallest building in the British Commonwealth, a record it held only briefly. More impressive was the overall extravagance, attention to detail and the cutting-edge facilities that people came to associate with the hotel. Impressively for the time, every single one of its hotel rooms included a bath, shower and personal radio.

It once dominated the city skyline, but as more and more high-rises have emerged around it, this is no longer the case. It has changed owners several times over the years, and the name above the door has been changed several times too, but one thing that remains the same is its commanding presence on the street.

CITY WITHIN A CITY

Due to its wealth of facilities the magnificent hotel became
known as 'a city within a city'. Here are some of the state-of-
the-art features of the original hotel:

1 048 rooms

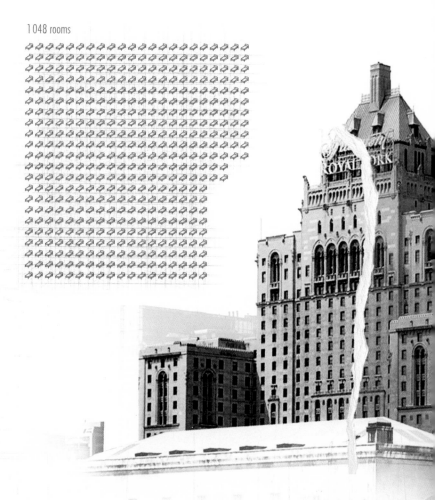

28 floors accessed by 10
ornate passenger lifts

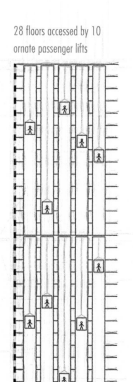

20-metre long telephone switchboard requiring 35 operators

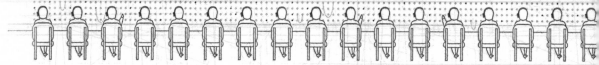

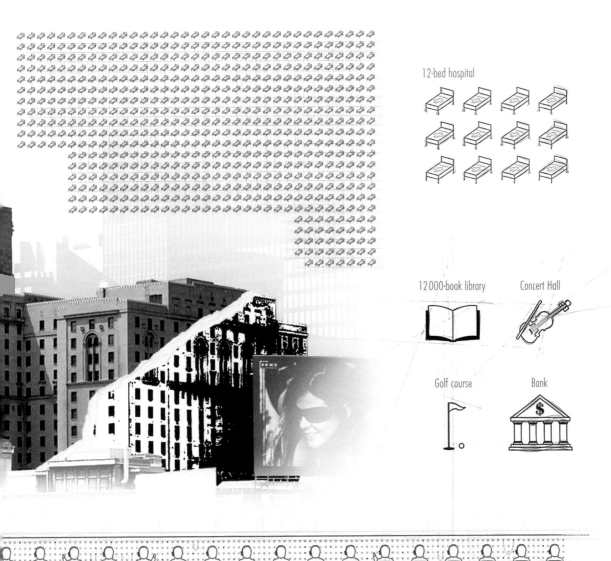

12-bed hospital

12 000-book library

Concert Hall

Golf course

Bank

BAKERY

The kitchen's bakery was capable of producing 15 000 French rolls a day.

GUESTS

Over the years, more than 40 million guests have passed through the hotel's doors, slightly more than the current population of Canada.

TALLEST IN CANADA

The Royal York was surpassed in height in 1931 by the office block Commerce Court North, just a few streets away, ending its short reign as Canada's, and the British Commonwealth's, tallest building.

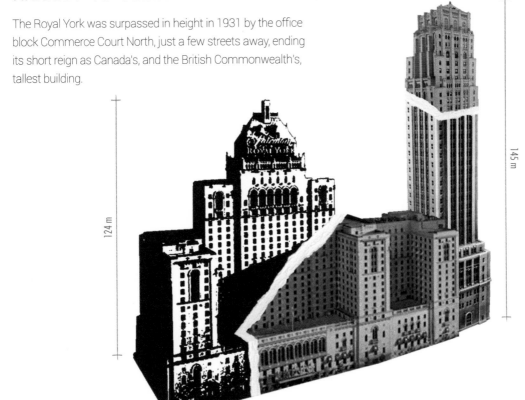

124 m

145 m

CONSTRUCTION:
1949–53

HEIGHT:
240.0 M

MOSCOW
RUSSIA

MOSCOW STATE UNIVERSITY

Russia's first skyscraper project, Palace of the Soviets, began shortly before World War II, but due to the conflict the project was suspended, with the framework's steel being reclaimed and used for defences. Shortly after the war, Stalin resumed his skyscraper plans, but instead of just the one, his vision was to include several dotted around the capital city. The idea being that, wherever you go in the city, you will always be able to see one of them. Stalin thought it was a blow to his country, and the communist ideology, that Moscow had no high-rises like in many capitalist countries, so he wanted to show the world that communism could be successful.

Nothing is known about the design process, or even about the sites' selection – a testament to Stalin's tight, secretive management style. Despite this we do know that the Moscow State University was the top priority, and the task of designing it was handed to Lev Rudnev and his team of architects. Rudnev was experienced and

his work was held in high regard by the Communist Party, having designed well-received government buildings before. He designed the university in the monumental Stalinist style, also taking influences from European Gothic cathedrals, and, as became commonplace with the set of seven skyscrapers (known as the Seven Sisters),

it was heavily over-engineered. Excessive use of steel in the building's framework and concrete throughout the structure made the building much weightier than necessary, due to their lack of experience and technology.

Work began on site in 1949, and the university building was inaugurated on 1 September 1953, having broken records to become the tallest building in Europe. It held on to the title until 1990 when the MesseTurm, a sixty-three-storey office building in Frankfurt, was completed.

BUILDING PLAN

The building's floor plan casts an unusual shape, the wings emanating from the central tower housing nine and eighteen-storey dormitory complexes. As the wings are such narrow structures they make the most of the available natural light.

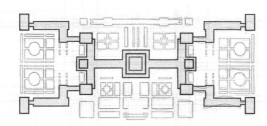

SEVEN SISTERS

The Seven Sisters is the name given to the group of high-rise buildings built in Moscow between 1947 and 1953, of which the main building, the Moscow State University, is the tallest. Incidentally, the term 'Seven Sisters' is not used or understood by the locals, they simply refer to them as *'Stalinskie Vysotki'* – Stalinist skyscrapers.

Hotel Ukraina
206 m

Kotelnicheskaya
Embankment Apartments
176 m

The Kudrinskaya
Square Building
160 m

The Hilton Moscow
Leningradskaya Hotel
136 m

STEEL

Although considerably shorter than the Empire State Building, the Moscow State University uses 90 per cent of the amount of structural steel because of its sprawling nature.

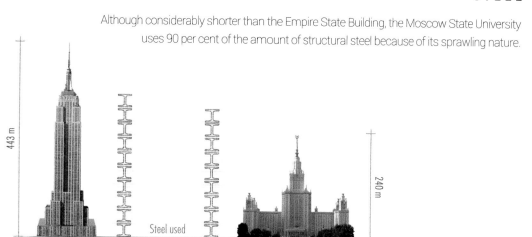

443 m

Steel used

240 m

The Main Building of
Moscow State University
240 m

The Ministry of Foreign
Affairs Main Building
172 m

The Red Gates
Administrative Building
133 m

MONUMENTAL EXCAVATIONS

The soil at the site was soft and the bedrock lay over 100 m beneath the surface, which posed some problems for the engineers. They devised a system that in essence was a reinforced-concrete box covering the area of the building, located below the ground. Due to the sheer size of the building the amount of earth displaced was equal in size to three Great Pyramids.

240.0 m

146.7 m

SPIRE

The delicate-looking spire at the top of the building is 57 m in length, and at the top sits an 11-tonne star.

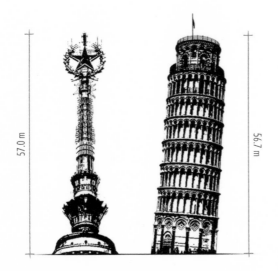

57.0 m

56.7 m

CORRIDORS

The university building has over 5 000 rooms which are connected by a colossal 33 km of corridors.

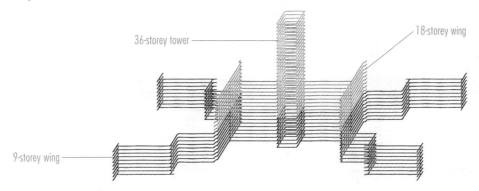

36-storey tower

18-storey wing

9-storey wing

HIGHER LEARNING

The Moscow State University is the tallest educational building in the world, even to this day. In second place is the Mode Gakuen Cocoon Tower in Japan that is home to a fashion school, a special technology and design college, and a medical college.

204 m

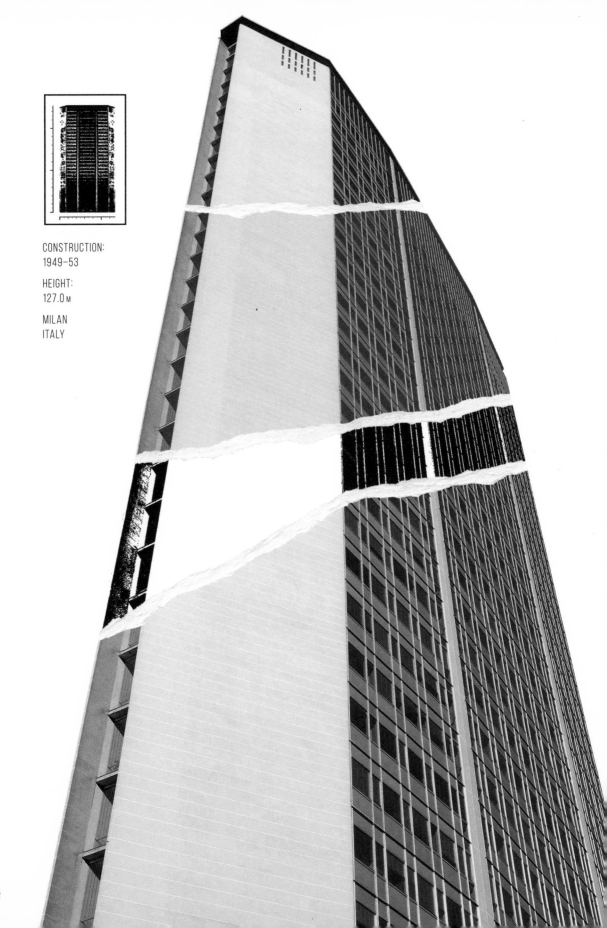

CONSTRUCTION:
1949–53

HEIGHT:
127.0 m

MILAN
ITALY

PIRELLI TOWER

The Pirelli Tower's elegant form ascends gracefully out of the ground, and despite it being the only tower in a predominantly low-rise area, its innovative design manages to project a sense of delicacy.

Alberto and Piero Pirelli, sons of the founder of the tyre company, looked to move their corporate offices to a different, more prestigious, location in Milan. The site chosen was previously one of the company tyre plants that was bombed in the war. Although not too impressive-sounding, the area had been green-lit by officials for planning permission for commercial buildings, and the town's train station had been recently relocated very close to the plot. Combined with the economic boom that Italy was undergoing after financially recovering from World War II, the area had the potential to become a thriving business district.

The brothers hired the services of Gio Ponti, a multi-talented designer who worked with ceramics, textiles, furniture and, of course, buildings. Although influenced by many different subjects, if it were possible to classify his style, it could be said that his work often induces an air of lightness. To realise his vision for the building he worked with Pier Nervi, a consummate expert in the understanding of concrete. He too was interested in lightness, especially how it can be achieved through the use of his preferred medium.

Together, Ponti and Nervi overcame the engineering hurdles of designing such a slender structure, the proportions of which made it highly susceptible to toppling. They succeeded not only in their engineering hurdles, but also in creating a symbol for the city of Milan, and a symbol of Italy's economic recovery.

FLOATING ROOF

The external walls of the building finish one storey below the roof. As the roof is supported by a secondary structure it appears to be floating above the building.

GAPS

The facade of each side of the building is bookended by concrete sections, running from the ground to the top floor, that conceal the stairwells and mechanical ducts. Oddly, the convex walls of each side's facade don't connect at either end of the building, but leave an air gap.

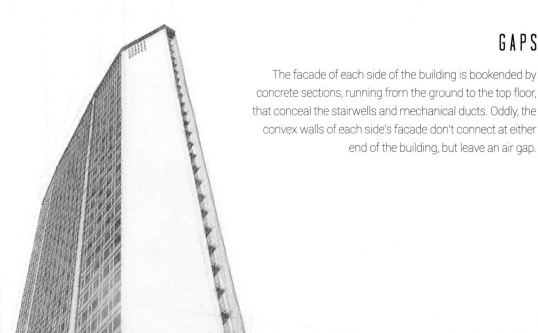

TAPERING CONCRETE

So that the building could support itself, the reinforced-concrete walls of the lower floors needed to be thicker than higher up the building in order to cope with the greater load.

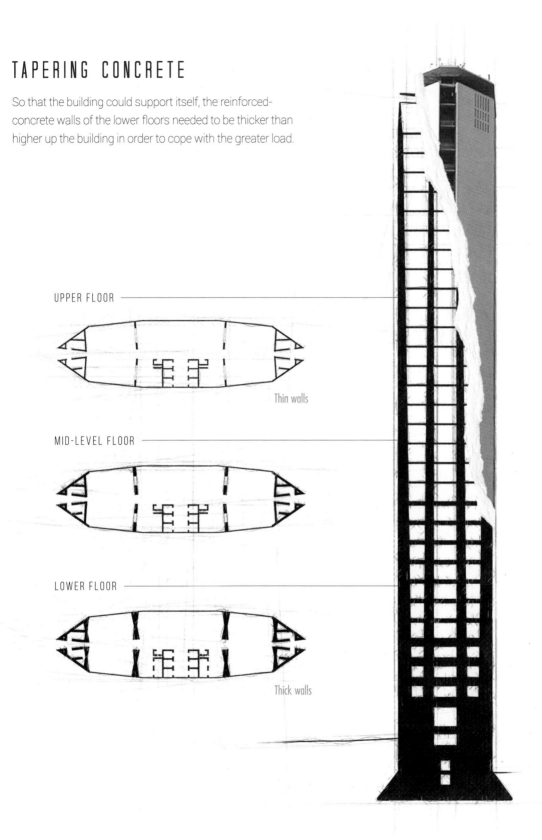

UPPER FLOOR

Thin walls

MID-LEVEL FLOOR

LOWER FLOOR

Thick walls

THE MADONNINA

According to local tradition, no building is allowed to rise higher than the Madonnina (the Virgin Mary) statue on top of Milan Cathedral. Out of respect for this custom, a miniaturised copy was installed on the roof of the tower, so that she still holds the top spot.

4.16 m

ORIGINAL

0.85 m

REPLICA

107 m

127 m

WIDER WINDOWS

The effect of the thinning concrete higher up the building can be witnessed from the outside. The supporting concrete walls, visible between the facades' glass, taper towards the top, and as a result the windows get wider.

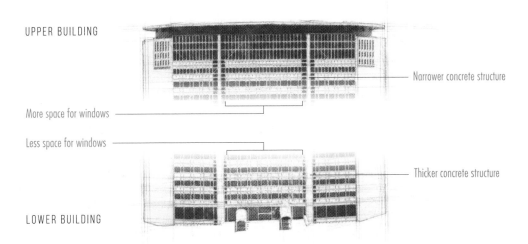

UPPER BUILDING

Narrower concrete structure

More space for windows

Less space for windows

Thicker concrete structure

LOWER BUILDING

OPTIMISING SPACE

As can be seen from the floor plan, the unusual lozenge shape of each storey works efficiently. The elevators, main staircases and washroom facilities are located centrally at the building's widest point, with office space and desks filling the space towards the tips of the building. As the building gets narrower at each end, so too does the corridor space that runs down the middle. The narrower sections of corridor correspond with areas that will receive less foot traffic.

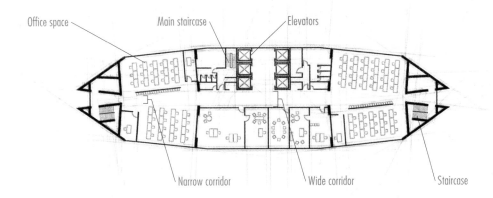

Office space

Main staircase

Elevators

Narrow corridor

Wide corridor

Staircase

CONSTRUCTION:
1954–8

HEIGHT:
156.9 M

NEW YORK
USA

SEAGRAM BUILDING

What makes the Seagram Building quite unique amongst the mass of skyscrapers that jostle for space in New York, is the room it allows itself. It stands coolly back from the street in front of an open plaza, in a place where land is ludicrously expensive. The open area that is left in front of the building is an audacious show of waste, but does convey a sense of importance, and the extra room means the architecture can be appreciated as a whole without having to crane the neck as is so often the case in the city.

Samuel Bronfman, CEO of Seagram, the massive distillery operation, required a new headquarters for his business, which had grown from strength to strength in the US after the prohibition era. He hired Ludwig Mies Van Der Rohe to design the building on the recommendation of his daughter Phyllis Lambert, also an architect. Mies was known for his 'less is more' approach to design, and for allowing structural elements of buildings to express themselves externally. In the

case of the Seagram, however, the vertical beams that run the height of the building are non-structural. For safety reasons, American building codes deemed that all structural steel be encased in a fireproof material. So, with concrete hiding the framework, Mies chose to suggest an underlying structure through the application of external non-load-bearing beams.

The simple form of the building – a rectangular block – combined with its lack of ornamentation and external-appearing structure, could have potentially made for an austere piece of architecture. Instead, by using rich materials such as bronze for the facade's beams, and exotic stone throughout, Mies created what he considered to be a 'pure' version of a steel-framed skyscraper. No need for decoration, the structure and form are aesthetically pleasing enough. Its relatively modest thirty-eight storeys has not hindered the building with regards to it being a masterpiece of functional aesthetics.

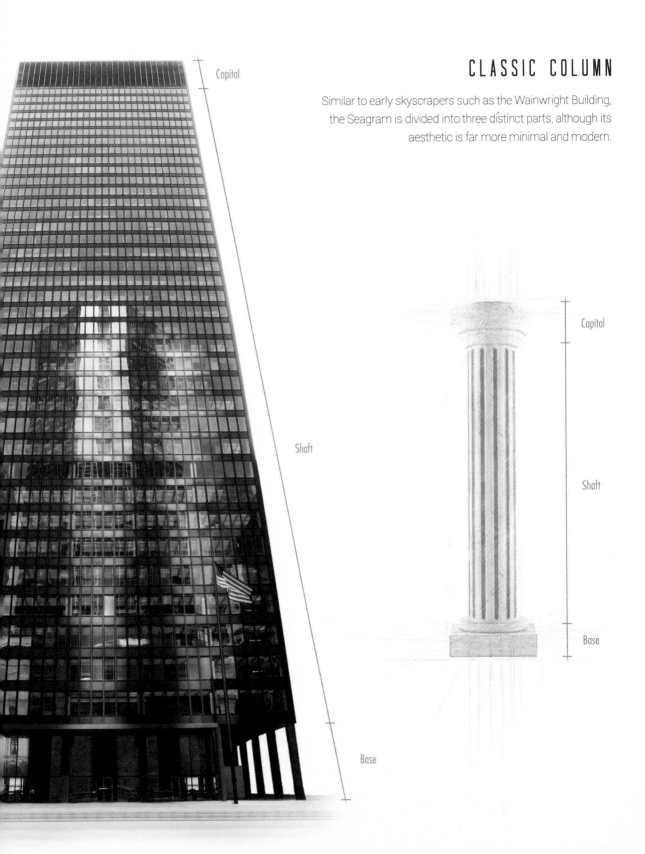

Capital

Shaft

Base

CLASSIC COLUMN

Similar to early skyscrapers such as the Wainwright Building, the Seagram is divided into three distinct parts, although its aesthetic is far more minimal and modern.

Capital

Shaft

Base

ROOM TO BREATHE

The Seagram Building only stands on 40 per cent of its zoning envelope. Most of the ground surface is covered by a granite-paved plaza, which extends underneath parts of the raised structure of the building. The tower is positioned 30 m back from the street, which was unusual as it was common practice to fill the entire plot at the time. By including the surrounding free space, Mies was able to create a rather unique building for New York, for if the whole plot had been filled, the building's design would have had to include setbacks to allow light to reach the streets.

Building footprint
(40%)

Columns

Tower

Pool

Free space
(60%)

30 m

The open area created by the plaza is also beneficial in allowing pedestrians to take in the building's powerful presence, a welcome experience in the tightly packed centre of New York. City officials were also impressed with the building's use of space, going so far as to amend zoning laws in 1961, encouraging developers to include areas open to the public.

FLOOR-TO-CEILING WINDOWS

The Seagram Building was the first skyscraper to have floor-to-ceiling windows.

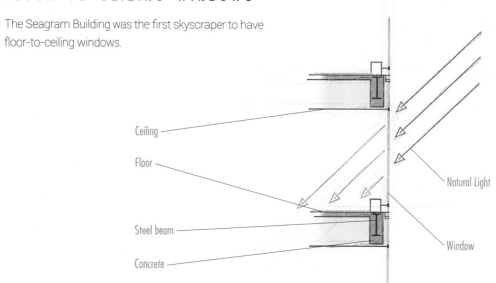

Ceiling

Floor

Steel beam

Concrete

Natural Light

Window

UNIFORM BLINDS

Mies was quite the perfectionist, and one thing he found disorderly was the way in which skyscraper windows appeared inconsistent, due to their blinds being open or closed by varying amounts. To bring some regularity to their appearance, he installed blinds that operated in three fixed positions: open, half-open, and closed.

BLIND
POSITIONS

Open

Half-open

Closed

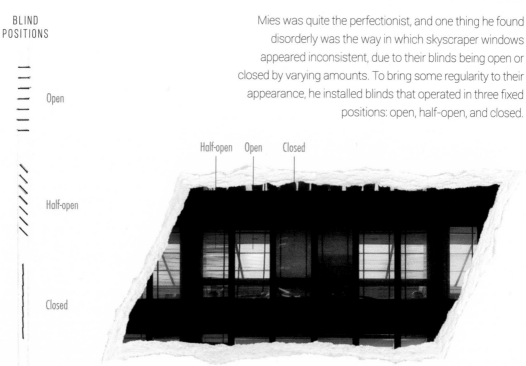

Half-open   Open   Closed

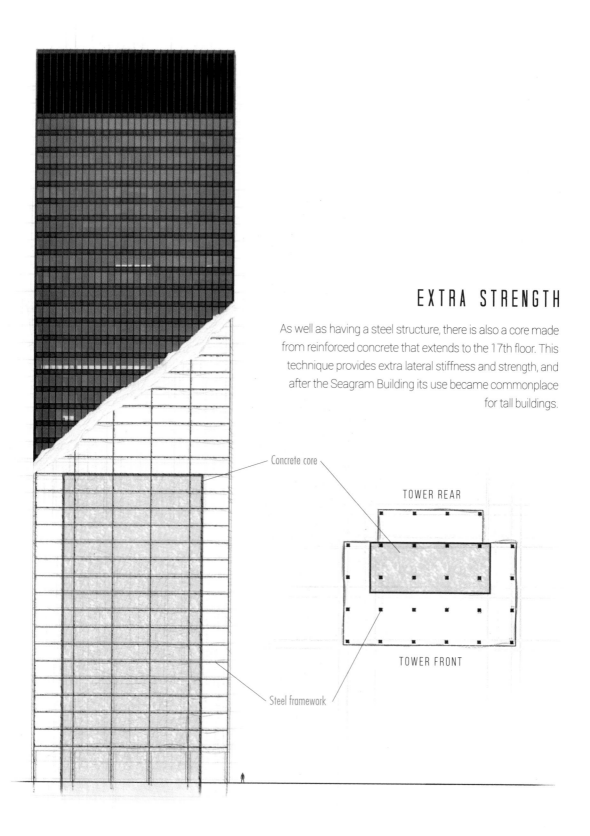

EXTRA STRENGTH

As well as having a steel structure, there is also a core made from reinforced concrete that extends to the 17th floor. This technique provides extra lateral stiffness and strength, and after the Seagram Building its use became commonplace for tall buildings.

Concrete core

TOWER REAR

TOWER FRONT

Steel framework

CONSTRUCTION:
1965–9

HEIGHT:
457.0 м

CHICAGO
USA

JOHN HANCOCK CENTER

Chicago, the birthplace of the skyscraper, had seen a flurry of architectural ingenuity and technological development around the turn of the 20th century. By the 1920s, however, the city had grown concerned about the rapid transformation that was happening, and brought in restrictions that effectively capped the height of skyscrapers to around twenty storeys. Fortunately, by the mid 1950s this cap had been lifted, and in the following decade computers capable of investigating new and different structural techniques were on the scene. It is against this backdrop that the John Hancock Center emerged.

The project was financed by John Hancock Mutual Life Insurance Co. It was originally conceived as two separate adjacent towers, one for offices and the other for apartments. There was, however, trouble buying the land that was needed, and because of advice from architect Bruce Graham and engineer Fazlur Khan the plan was altered. Their main concern was that residents of the apartment building would be able to see into the windows of the office block, and vice versa. The 100-storey building they proposed placed the residential floors above the offices for better views, along with an observation deck and restaurant at the top. The first six floors would be made up of commercial space and parking. The building took on a tapering nature, in part for stability, but also due to its function. The larger floor plates lower down the building are more suited to office use, and the smaller floor plates near the top allow for better natural lighting in the apartments.

Most striking is the John Hancock Center's external cross-bracing that shifts the structure onto the outside of the building, opening up floor space inside. This system of tubular bracing provides excellent resistance to lateral forces, reducing sway and improving comfort high up the building. The strength of the design is proven by the reduction in necessary materials: the amount of steel used is equivalent to that of a forty-five-storey building.

FASTEST ELEVATORS

When constructed, the building's fifty elevators were the fastest in the western hemisphere, capable of taking passengers from the ground floor all the way to the 95th in 38 seconds, at a top speed of 33.5 kilometres per hour. By comparison, the Woolworth Building's elevators, which were cutting edge less than sixty years before, would have only made it to the 30th floor in the same time.

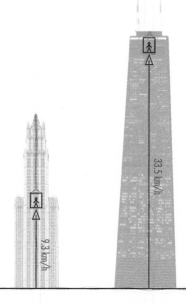

9.3 km/h

33.5 km/h

ANTENNAE

The east antenna is the taller of the two, measuring 106 m, and the west one is about 7 m shorter. The building therefore owes over a fifth of its total height to the antennae, both of which are taller than Big Ben.

96 m

106 m

SLOPING WALLS

The tapered nature of the building is the result of a number of factors. A box-shaped skyscraper's weight is distributed more evenly throughout its height, but the John Hancock Center's broad base and narrow roof lower the building's centre of mass, resulting in a more stable structure. Being narrower at the top also means that it will endure less wind force, especially as wind speeds increase at higher altitudes. In terms of the building's function, the way in which each floor's area diminishes with height is quite apt. At the top of the building are the residential floors which suit the smaller, more personal, areas. The floors below open up to accommodate office space, and below these are the even larger commercial levels and the wide plaza.

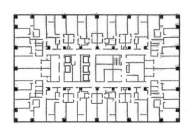

TYPICAL APARTMENT FLOOR

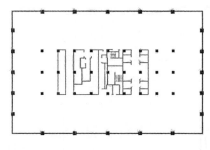

TYPICAL OFFICE FLOOR

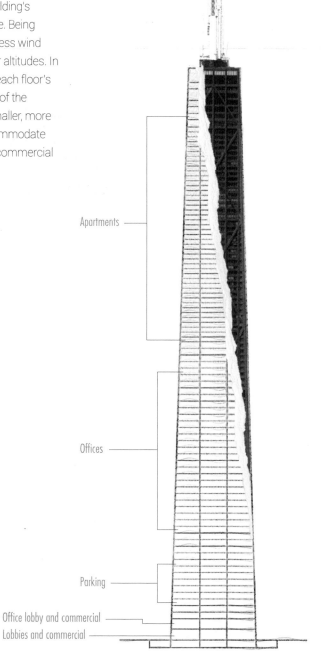

Apartments

Offices

Parking

Office lobby and commercial

Lobbies and commercial

RESTRICTED VIEW

As the exterior cross-bracing can obstruct the view from the apartment windows, sometimes quite drastically, it has a noticeable effect on property value.

STEEL

The 46 000 tonnes of steel used on the building could have produced 33 000 cars.

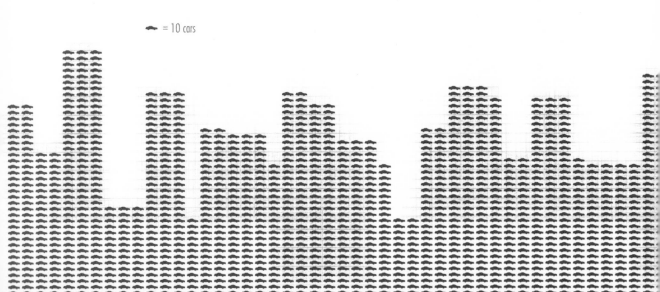

= 10 cars

WIND RESISTANCE

Chicago is known as 'the windy city', and as the nickname suggests, tall buildings built here must be able to withstand the Chicago winds. The building's structure can be heard creaking and groaning on windy days; however, it performs well and remains rigid – the tip of the building's antennae only sway about 20 cm. Inside, all that can be noticed is a slight motion of the liquid inside drinking glasses.

CONSTRUCTION:
1969–72

HEIGHT:
260.0 M

SAN FRANCISCO
USA

TRANSAMERICA PYRAMID

Today the Transamerica Pyramid is a landmark feature on the San Francisco skyline, yet when its designs were unveiled to the public in 1969, the building was faced with derision and protests. Its architect, William Pereira, was widely known for his movie-set designs and futuristic buildings, and locals were concerned that his 'unreal' aesthetic would not fit in with the area's quite conservative architecture.

The building was commissioned by Transamerica CEO Jack Beckett to be the company's headquarters, and it was he who inspired the form the building would take. Beckett claimed that he wanted light to be able to reach the streets below, and so Pereira set to work designing his postmodern pyramid. The tapering design also conveniently adhered to San Francisco's strict guidelines regarding how

floor area should diminish with height. Also highly beneficial, especially in such a geologically active area, was the design's effect on making the structure more stable.

In defiance of its detractors, the Transamerica Pyramid's construction went ahead and its doors opened in 1972. Despite its initial frosty reception, the public gradually warmed to it, and the building has since received high critical acclaim. As the tallest building in the United States west of the Mississippi River, its height and striking appearance helped boost the profile of its parent company. Although Transamerica Corp. have now moved their headquarters from the building, they still retain a presence there, and they still continue to use the image of the building in their logo.

FORM

Conceptually, the building's form was inspired by the towering sequoia redwood trees that are native to the region. The trees' conical form allows for light to reach the forest floor, just as the Transamerica Pyramid allows light to reach street level.

WINGS

The two wings that protrude at the top of the building increase the useable floor space by containing the building's services. The east wing contains the shaft for the two elevators that can reach the top floor, and the west wing contains a stairwell which also acts as a smoke evacuation tower in case of fire.

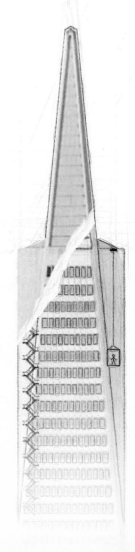

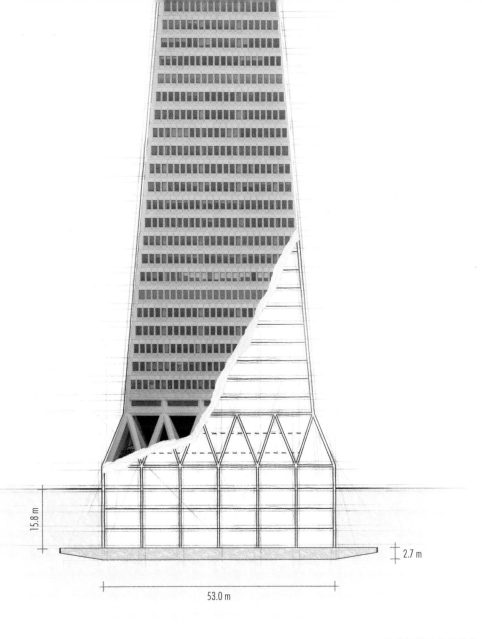

15.8 m

2.7 m

53.0 m

STRUCTURE

The construct rests on a 2.7-metre thick reinforced-concrete raft, which is the size of the building's plot and set only 15 m below ground. The foundations' concrete was poured continuously, day and night, for three days, taking 1 750 truckloads. To strengthen it, it was poured over 480 km of steel reinforcement bars. The compact foundations are designed to move in the event of an earthquake, so as not to transmit the movement of the shaking ground up the building. At ground level, flared trusses are designed to handle the vertical forces incurred by the mass of the building, as well as horizontal forces that occur during earthquakes. On top of this structure sits the pyramid-shaped part of the building, which comprises an outer frame and four inner frames.

WINDOWS

The majority of the building's 3 678 windows pivot 360° around their central axes. As the building has an unconventional shape it makes it harder to clean using conventional means, and so the windows were designed like this to make it easier.

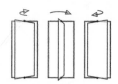

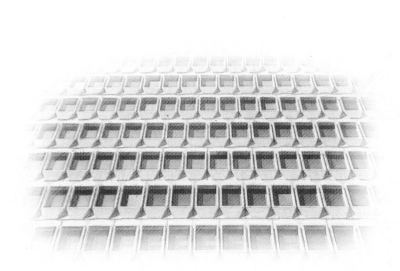

EARTHQUAKE

In 1989 the Loma Prieta earthquake shook the area violently, causing the Transamerica Pyramid to shake for about a minute. The building performed well, though, with the top swaying by only 30 cm. There was no damage, and no serious injuries inside the building.

STOREYS

Due to the nature of the building's design, the usable floor space decreases greatly with height. The 5th floor has the most space, and the 48th floor has the least, at less than 10 per cent of the area in comparison.

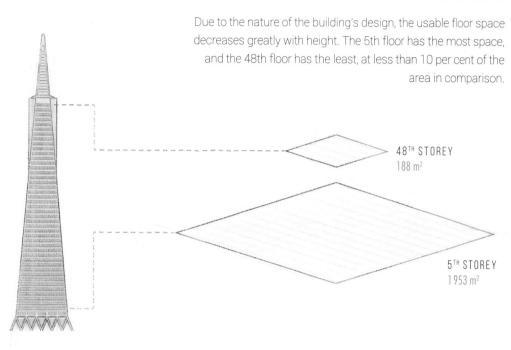

48ᵀᴴ STOREY
188 m²

5ᵀᴴ STOREY
1 953 m²

NEW AND OLD

The Great Pyramid at Giza was the tallest man-made structure for millennia, but through technological advancements we can now reach far higher, while using far fewer materials.

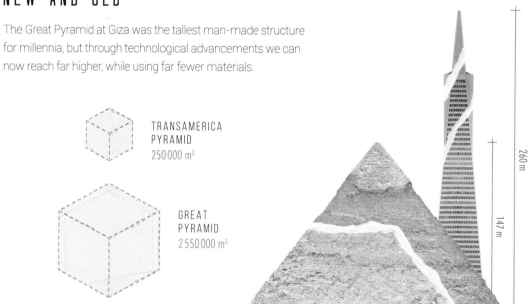

TRANSAMERICA PYRAMID
250 000 m³

GREAT PYRAMID
2 550 000 m³

260 m

147 m

CONSTRUCTION:
1985–90

HEIGHT:
367.4 m

HONG KONG
CHINA

Bank of China Tower

Hong Kong's central business district is famous for its multitude of skyscrapers, one of the most noticeable of which is the Bank of China Tower (BOC Tower). The building stands out, in part, because of the distinctive structural cross-bracing on its external surfaces. The bracing is highly visible day or night; in the daytime its white finish contrasts with the blue glass that it's set in, and by night the runs of framework are illuminated against the black. The striking, ever-present triangular shapes formed by the bracing are reminiscent of the folds found in origami, and they convey that the building somehow unfolded itself upwards into being.

The initial concept for the building came about shortly after the British agreed to hand Hong Kong back to mainland China. The state-run bank was eager to commemorate the occasion, not only the nation's reunification, but its emergence as an international financial power. Hiring Chinese-born American architect I. M. Pei, who was noted for his work on tall buildings and for his use of triangular forms, they set about creating a tower to really capture the aspirations of the Chinese people.

Many obstacles were to be overcome in the BOC Tower's construction. The relatively small site (two acres) was on steeply sloping ground, and access to the confined area was made near impossible by the highways that surrounded the plot on three sides. Also, due to Hong Kong's location in a typhoon zone, buildings of this height pose significant challenges, and the earthquake guidelines are four times more strict than LA's. Pei met these problems head on, and his completed building became the tallest in Asia and, at over 300 m in height, the first supertall skyscraper outside the US.

COMPONENT PARTS

The BOC Tower's four triangular towers interlock to form a square-shaped building plan. Each tower is topped with a sloping roof that is inclined towards the centre of the building.

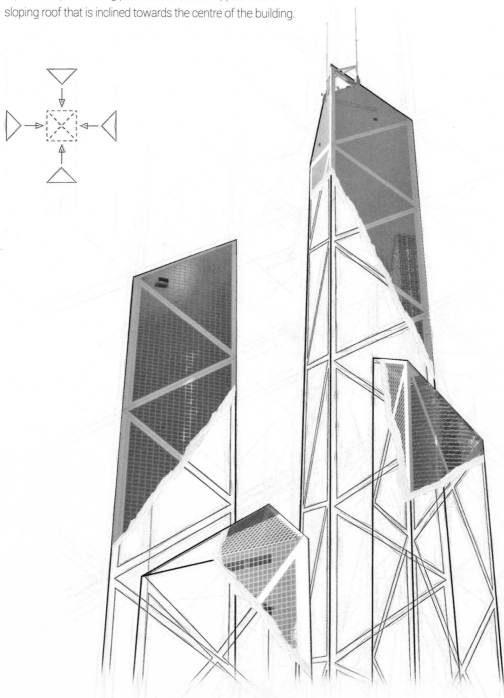

STRUCTURE

Most of the weight of the building is transferred to the ground by the four huge steel columns positioned at the corners. A fifth column is located in the centre, which provides extra strength at the point where the four sections all meet.

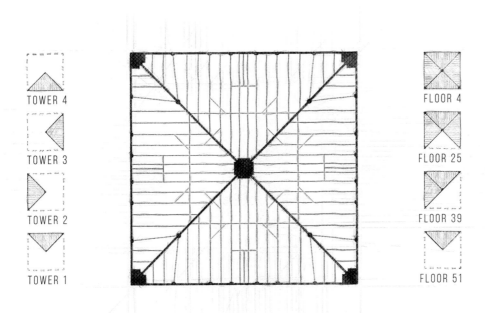

TOWER 4

TOWER 3

TOWER 2

TOWER 1

FLOOR 4

FLOOR 25

FLOOR 39

FLOOR 51

SPACE FRAME

The BOC Tower is the first composite high-rise building to use a space frame. Space frames are used in all sorts of structural engineering, such as vehicle chassis and bridge building. They are made by using interlocking struts in geometric patterns that make use of the inherent rigidity of the triangle. The strength of the frames means that fewer vertical supports are needed throughout the building, freeing up floor space.

BAMBOO

The growth patterns of bamboo are said to have been a significant inspiration for the design of the building. In Chinese culture bamboo is a symbol of strength and growth.

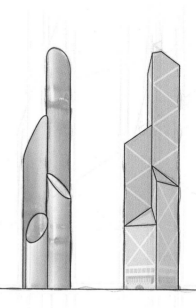

FENG SHUI

In Hong Kong it is normal for a feng shui master to approve and sign a developer's draft before they apply for a building permit. The BOC Tower was the first major building in Hong Kong to sidestep this procedure, which caused some dismay. Some feng shui practitioners were opposed to the sharp edges and the many 'X' shapes in the design, as the shape is commonly linked with death. Pei took this on board, making some minor tweaks to his plans, reducing the amount of threatening 'X's by replacing them with softer triangle shapes.

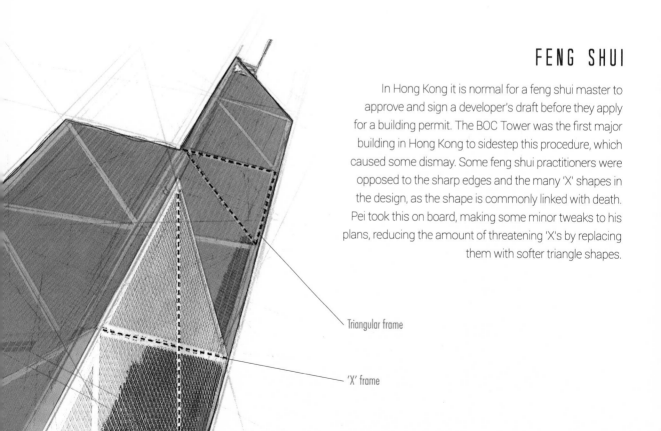

Triangular frame

'X' frame

TALLEST BUILDING OUTSIDE THE USA

When it was completed, the BOC Tower was the tallest building in the world outside
the US, and also the first to surpass 305 m (1 000 ft). It overtook The Hopewell Centre
to become Asia's tallest building and was itself beaten, in 1992, by Central Plaza.

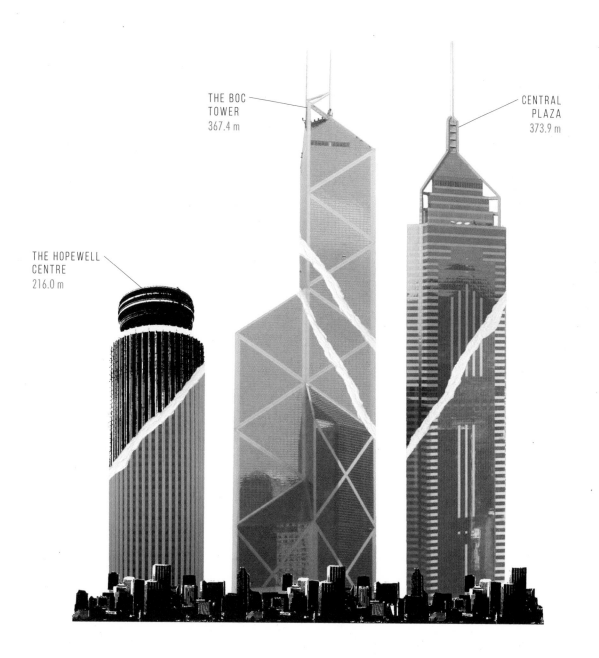

THE BOC
TOWER
367.4 m

CENTRAL
PLAZA
373.9 m

THE HOPEWELL
CENTRE
216.0 m

CONSTRUCTION:
1994–7

HEIGHT:
328.0 M

AUCKLAND
NEW ZEALAND

SKY TOWER

The Sky Tower is similar to the Eiffel Tower in that it is not a continuously habitable building, but it is indeed a tower, and is also its respective city's most defining landmark. And just as the Eiffel Tower broke engineering records, so too did the Sky Tower, most notably for being the tallest free-standing structure in the southern hemisphere.

The tower is part of a casino complex, which at the time was run by Harrah's Entertainment, and the two were built alongside each other. Its observation decks offer visitors unimpeded views of Auckland, with views of over 80 km from its uppermost deck. The Sky Tower also offers the chance to dine peacefully 190 m in the air, in New Zealand's only revolving restaurant, or more casually in a brasserie-style eatery on the floor above. Other more physical activities also take place at the top of the tower, such as bungee jumping or the skywalk, where visitors can walk around the structure 192 m up, on a path only 1.2 m wide. In spite of the frivolous fun to be had

here, the tower's primary function is a radio and telecommunications mast, hosting the world's largest single FM radio transmitter.

The Sky Tower was designed by New Zealand architect Gordon Moller, whose initial proposals for the structure saw it clad in aluminium with a satin finish, giving the structure a more futuristic, high-tech feel. This idea was dismissed for financial reasons, and the tower's shaft was finished with smooth concrete. As with any tall building, there were hurdles for the design and construction teams to deal with, but unlike most tall buildings the Sky Tower was completed an impressive six months ahead of schedule.

OBSERVATION DECKS

The Sky Tower has three observation decks, a cafe and a restaurant, each on their own level.

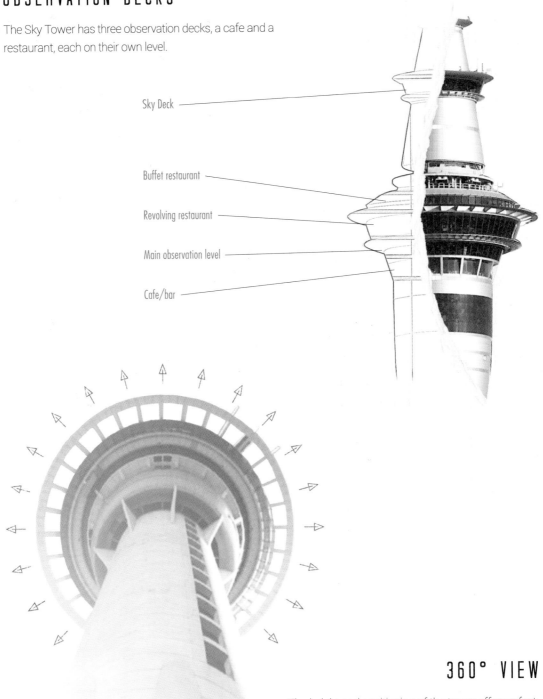

Sky Deck

Buffet restaurant

Revolving restaurant

Main observation level

Cafe/bar

360° VIEW

The height and positioning of the tower offer perfect, uninterrupted views of Auckland.

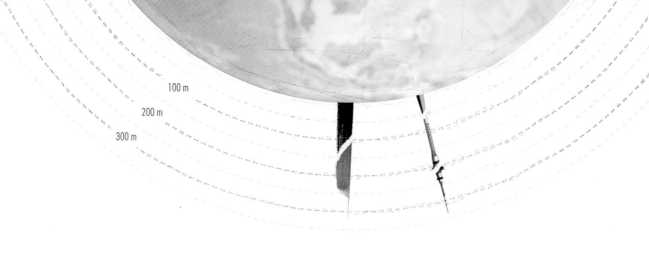

100 m

200 m

300 m

TALLEST IN THE SOUTHERN HEMISPHERE

The Sky Tower is the tallest free-standing structure in the southern hemisphere, closely followed by the Q1 in Queensland.

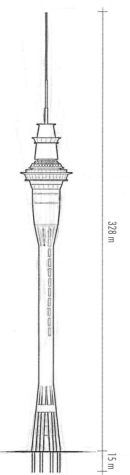

328 m

15 m

SHALLOW FOUNDATIONS

To look at the structure one might assume the foundations go deep into the ground, especially due to the bulk of the building making it look top-heavy. However, the eight foundation legs, supported by sixteen piles, only reach 15 m into the ground. In spite of this the construct is able to withstand an earthquake with a magnitude of 8.0 at a proximity of 20 km.

FOUNDATION
LEGS PLAN

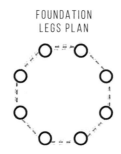

BUILDING ACCURACY

To stay upright, it is imperative that a narrow structure such as this is perfectly perpendicular. Along with ground-based measurements and the use of lasers to project precise reference marks, seven different global positioning satellites relayed information to the construction team for pinpoint accuracy.

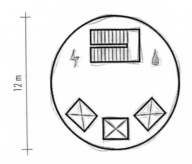

12 m

SHAFT

The tower's supporting shaft contains the three elevators, stairwell and services.

TOWERS

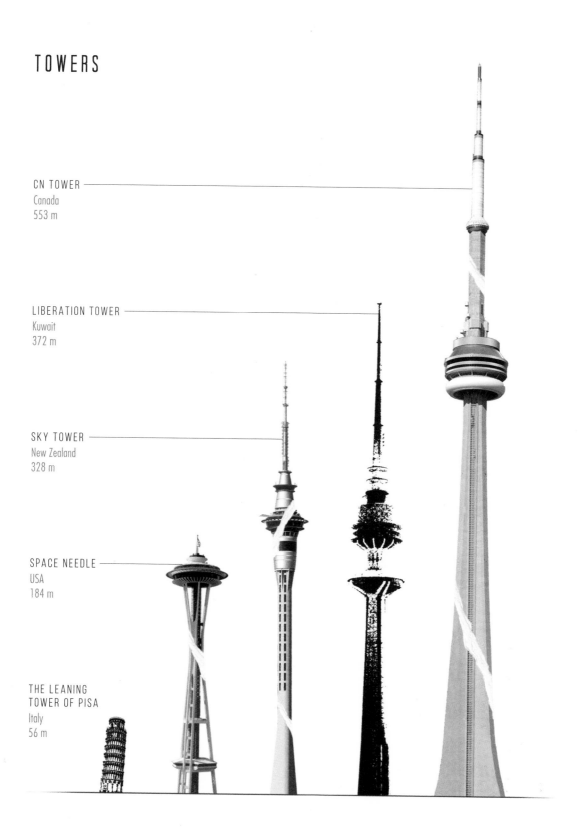

CN TOWER
Canada
553 m

LIBERATION TOWER
Kuwait
372 m

SKY TOWER
New Zealand
328 m

SPACE NEEDLE
USA
184 m

THE LEANING
TOWER OF PISA
Italy
56 m

MODERN MASTERPIECES

Architects have continued to push the boundaries of architectural possibilities as demand soars around the globe, creating ever more original and wondrous towers. There seems to be no end to the hunger of nations and big businesses for high-profile architecture, used as a means of self-promotion, and for putting themselves on the map. In the modern world no idea is too extreme.

The exponential advances in computer technology have allowed architects to create increasingly complex models and simulations, giving them the freedom to create structures that spiral, warp and twist. The jaw-dropping dimensions and shapes of modern skyscrapers no longer seem to be limited by the laws of physics, but only by wealth, and the imagination of the architect. Improvements in technology have also resulted in buildings of greater sustainability and better energy efficiency, in compliance with our growing concerns about Earth's climate. Concrete has been developed that can not only withstand much greater pressures than in the last century, but also absorbs less heat, along with higher grade glass that reflects more UV light.

Thriving financial markets in China and East Asia have spurred on the growth of some of the world's tallest skyscrapers. As China's appetite for goods and services

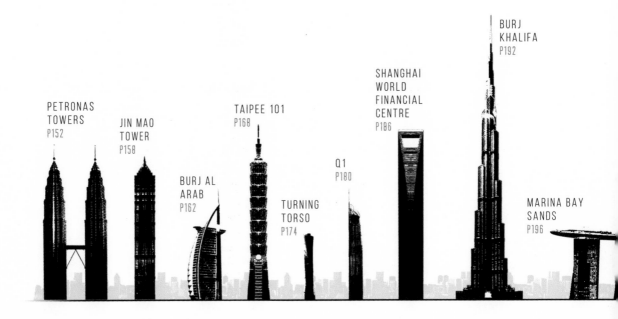

PETRONAS
TOWERS
P152

JIN MAO
TOWER
P158

BURJ AL
ARAB
P162

TAIPEE 101
P168

TURNING
TORSO
P174

Q1
P180

SHANGHAI
WORLD
FINANCIAL
CENTRE
P186

BURJ
KHALIFA
P192

MARINA BAY
SANDS
P196

grows, people are flocking to the cities in their millions, where opportunities and wages are more appealing. In much the same way as the buildings in New York over a hundred years ago, the only way to go is up.

Another region that has emerged as an ambassador for the supertall is the Middle East. Yet the conventional pattern of high population density combined with high land values producing high buildings does not apply here. For example, The Burj Khalifa in Dubai stands in a city where space is abundant, yet it broke the record for the world's tallest building. With that, it has succeeded in putting Dubai on the map, as have other landmark towers that signify the region's shift from being a singularly oil-based economy to one that has moved into service-based sectors.

Our love of skyscrapers shows no signs of slowing. Just as one record is broken, another building is being designed to break it again – a pattern that seems to be repeating ad infinitum. How much higher can we go? Maybe soon we will reach the limits of our ingenuity and resources. Or, maybe, one day even the Burj Khalifa will be looked down upon.

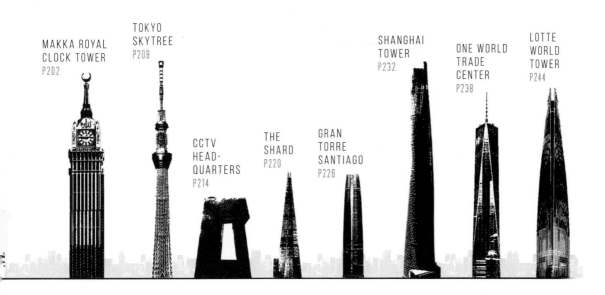

MAKKA ROYAL CLOCK TOWER
P202

TOKYO SKYTREE
P208

CCTV HEAD-QUARTERS
P214

THE SHARD
P220

GRAN TORRE SANTIAGO
P226

SHANGHAI TOWER
P232

ONE WORLD TRADE CENTER
P238

LOTTE WORLD TOWER
P244

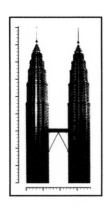

CONSTRUCTION:
1993–6

HEIGHT:
451.9 M

KUALA LUMPUR
MALAYSIA

PETRONAS TOWERS

The Petronas Towers were the first buildings to break the US's streak of having the world's tallest skyscraper for over a hundred years, bringing the title to Malaysia, and putting Kuala Lumpur on the map. To this day they are the tallest twin towers on earth, and the premier tourist attraction in the thriving city.

Argentine architect Cesar Pelli was commissioned by Malaysia's national oil company Petronas to create a 21st-century icon for the city. As well as looking forward, they wanted the building to reflect the country it represents and embrace its culture, and so Pelli proceeded with his postmodern designs.

As Islam is Malaysia's most prominent religion, Islamic geometries are referenced throughout the towers' final design. It is, however, the sheer scale of the buildings that speaks the loudest. As if breaking the world record once wasn't enough, they broke it twice.

Due to the Malaysian government imposing a time limit of six years from the start of excavation, two construction firms were hired to get the work done. Tower 1 was built by a Japanese construction consortium, and Tower 2 by a South Korean consortium. The foundations for the eighty-eight-storey twin towers were the deepest of any structure at the time, owing not just to the immense size of the buildings, but the choice of using reinforced concrete over steel. At the time of construction, imported steel was very costly, and although concrete was good for sway reduction, it would make the building twice as heavy.

In spite of an early issue with a batch of concrete failing a strength test that caused work to be halted, the project was completed in good time, with Tower 2 topping out first. The buildings were finally finished on 1 March 1996, with the completion of the spires.

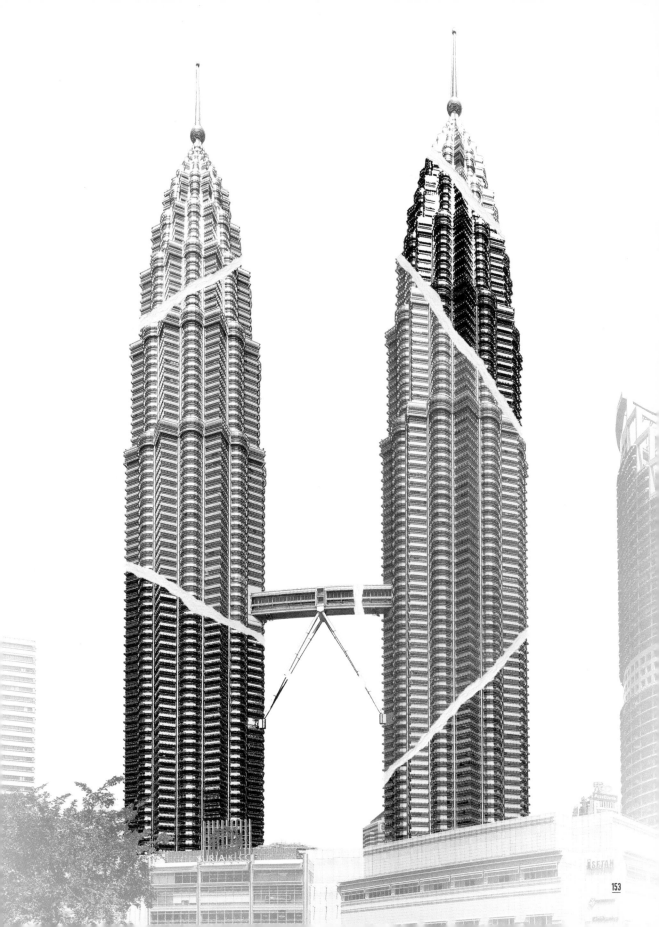

58 m

170 m

SKYBRIDGE

Located between the 41st and 42nd floors of the towers, the Skybridge is the highest two-storey bridge in the world. It is not rigidly attached to the towers to prevent it from breaking; instead it slides in and out of the structures using a system of expansion joints, hinges and spherical bearings.

ISLAMIC INSPIRATION

Early designs by Pelli were rejected by the prime minister for not reflecting Malaysian culture well enough. In subsequent redesigns, Pelli overlaid geometric shapes, in a fashion reminiscent of Islamic forms, to create the floor plan and influence the overall shape of the building. The two overlapping squares form an eight-pointed star that represents unity and harmony in Islamic culture, and the circular sections that were added were done so to maximise floor space.

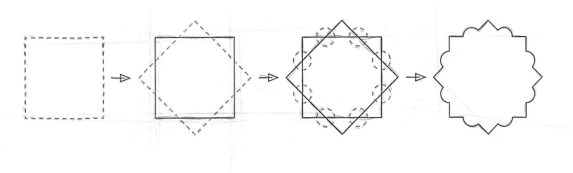

STRUCTURE

Importing enough steel to build the towers would have been too costly, so the towers were innovatively built using super-high-strength reinforced concrete. More effective than steel at reducing a building's sway, its downside is that it can make a building twice as heavy. The tube-in-tube design that had become commonplace on tall buildings was created in this instance by a square-shaped shaft that is surrounded by sixteen gigantic columns.

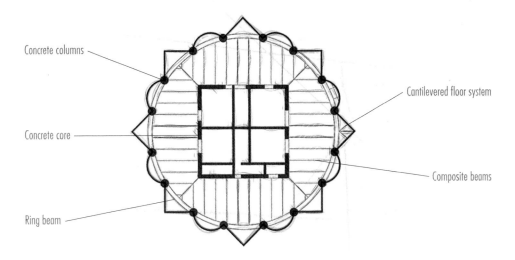

Concrete columns

Cantilevered floor system

Concrete core

Composite beams

Ring beam

ANNEXES

Each tower has a forty-four-storey annex attached to it to provide extra office space. Despite being dwarfed by the towers they accompany, they would be huge buildings in their own right.

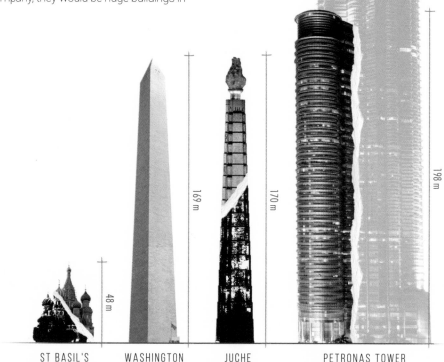

ST BASIL'S CATHEDRAL	WASHINGTON MONUMENT	JUCHE TOWER	PETRONAS TOWER ANNEX
48 m	169 m	170 m	198 m

ELEVATORS

There are thirty-eight elevators in each tower, most of which are double-decked. The double-deck elevators can hold twenty-six people on each deck, with the top deck accessing only odd-numbered floors, and the bottom deck those that are even-numbered. Someone in the lobby wanting to reach an odd-numbered floor must take an escalator up to the top deck of the elevator.

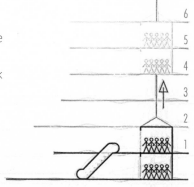

FOUNDATIONS

From the start of the site's excavation to completing the foundations took a full year. Huge amounts of earth needed excavating, a multitude of concrete piles were to be driven deep underground, and the longest concrete pour in Malaysian history would have to take place before work on the structure could begin.

1 The site is excavated to a depth great enough to hold a five-storey building.

21 m

2 104 concrete piles were then driven into the ground beneath each tower's location.

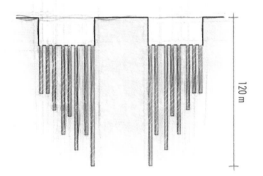

120 m

3 Concrete was poured to form a raft on top of the piles. The pouring took fifty-four hours straight, with each concrete truck arriving every two and a half minutes.

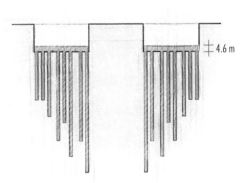

4.6 m

4 Building of the structure commenced on 1 April 1994, once the foundations were completed.

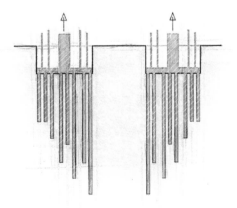

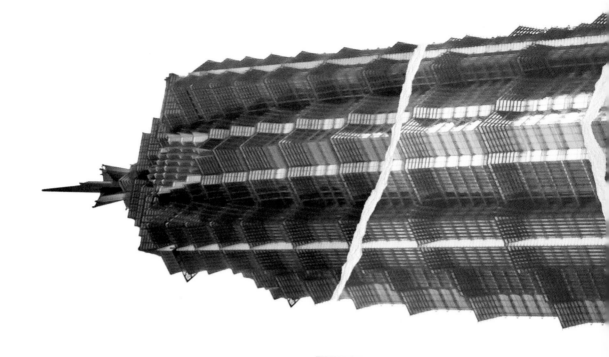

CONSTRUCTION:
1994–9

HEIGHT:
420.5 м

SHANGHAI
CHINA

JIN MAO TOWER

Today the Jin Mao Tower stands shoulder to shoulder with two other supertalls (buildings over 300 m), a sign of the country's prosperity since straying from its communist roots. It was the first of the three towers to appear on the scene after Shanghai was visited in 1990 by Deng Xiaoping, a Chinese revolutionary and politician, who had led the People's Republic of China until his

The client, China Shanghai Foreign Trade Centre, requested that the number 8 play a role in the building's design. In Chinese culture, 8 is said to be a lucky number associated with prosperity and wealth, highly appropriate for such a financial investment. With this in mind, the building's highest accessible floor (the observation deck) is floor 88, and each setback's height is 1/8 less than the one below.

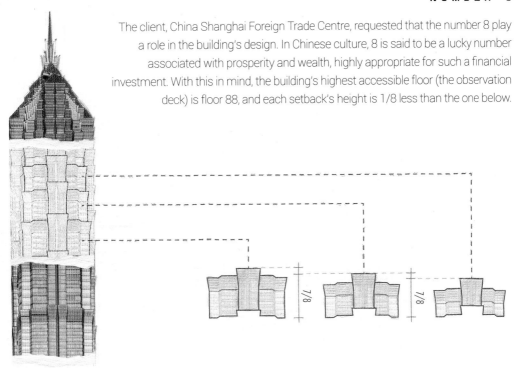

FUNCTION

The Jin Mao Tower's main tenant is the five-star Grand Hyatt Shanghai hotel that resides in the upper half of the building. The rest of the building is mostly used for office space, along with various amenities, such as shops and restaurants, near ground level.

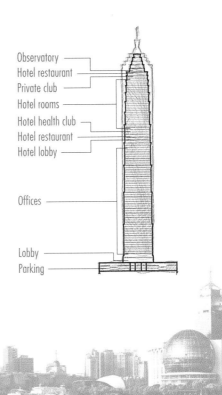

Observatory
Hotel restaurant
Private club
Hotel rooms
Hotel health club
Hotel restaurant
Hotel lobby

Offices

Lobby
Parking

The eighty-eight-storey building is home to various occupants, most notable of which is the five-star hotel that occupies floors 53 to 87. As one of the highest hotels in the world, spectacular views are a given, and the interior is just as impressive. Starting from the 56th floor, an atrium extends up to the 87th, creating an open space inside the building that reaches approximately 115 m from the lobby floor to the ceiling.

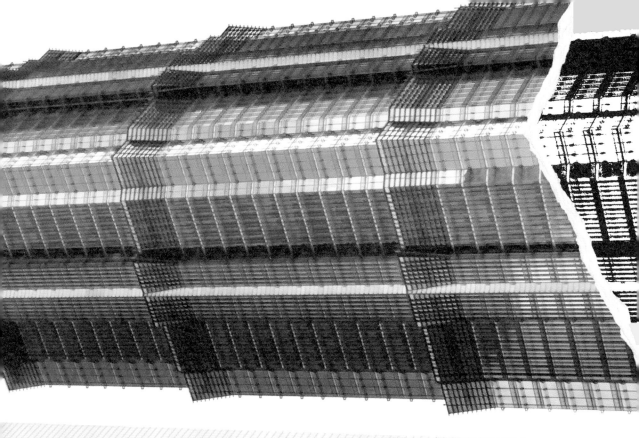

retirement the previous year. Xiaoping was the man responsible for China's economic reforms that had opened up their markets to the global economy, and who saw the potential in transforming Shanghai into the financial centre of the nation. Xiaoping urged the city's municipal government to invest in the Pudong district, a largely neglected area of the city. Within months the area was flattened and ready to be transformed.

Chicago firm Skidmore, Owings & Merrill (SOM) were the architects brought on board for the project. One of the largest architectural firms in the world, SOM have offices internationally and have carried out projects in over fifty countries. The company was founded in 1937 and has become primarily renowned for high-end commercial buildings, and has designed many of the world's tallest buildings. In the same vein as the Petronas Towers, the SOM designs were intended to capture the spirit and history of the region, while creating a new-age technical marvel. This they achieved, creating a beautifully proportioned tapered structure clad in a sleek aluminium lattice frame, yet one that is also instantly recognisable as having its roots in China's original skyscraper – the pagoda.

STRUCTURE

The concrete core of the tube-in-tube structure rises from the foundations all the way to floor 87. The number 8 comes into play again, as the core's steel outriggers attach to 8 composite mega-columns that form the outer structure. There are also 8 steel columns that form the outer shell of the structure which provide extra strength.

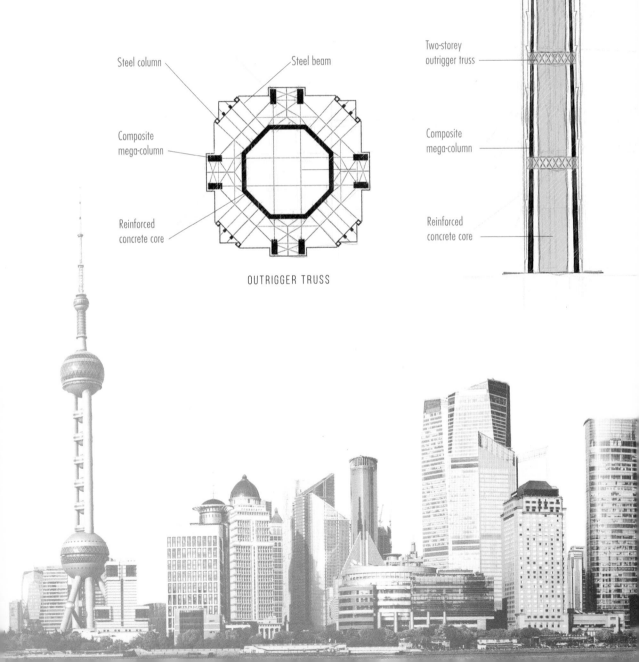

Steel column

Steel beam

Composite
mega-column

Reinforced
concrete core

OUTRIGGER TRUSS

Two-storey
outrigger truss

Composite
mega-column

Reinforced
concrete core

SWIMMING POOL

The swimming pool on the 57th floor is one of the highest in the world and boasts amazing views of Shanghai. It also benefits the building by acting as a damper against lateral movement of the structure in the wind. As the water is not bound to the structure, and its mass is quite significant, its inertia causes it to push back against the building's sway.

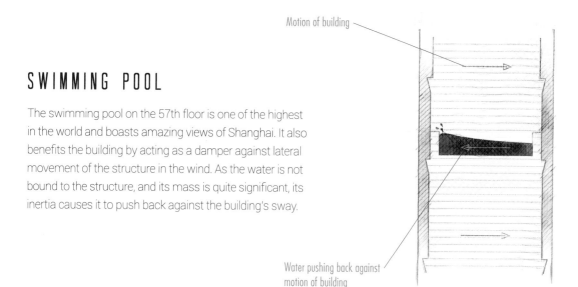

Motion of building

Water pushing back against motion of building

ANCIENT INFLUENCE

The tower's design is rooted in ancient Chinese architecture. The setbacks and ornamentation it features are reminiscent of the tiered pagodas that are strewn throughout the country's landscape.

Great Wild Goose Pagoda of Xi'an (7th century)

CONSTRUCTION:
1994–9

HEIGHT:
321.0 м

DUBAI
UAE

BURJ AL ARAB

Today, Dubai is an internationally known hub of tourism, trade and finance, with some of the most ostentatious skyscrapers on the planet. However, if you compare its skyline now to that of the mid 1990s, the place seems unrecognisable. When construction started on the man-made island on which the Burj Al Arab hotel sits, development of the area was in its infancy, and as such the Burj Al Arab was Dubai's first major landmark.

The spate of glistening high-rises that have raced to the skies above Dubai are a result of the area's wealth, sparked by the oil boom of the 1970s and the vision of its ruler, Sheikh Mohammed bin Rashid Al Maktoum. Wanting to create an iconic building that would become a beacon for the city, he contacted Atkins, a London-based multidisciplinary consultancy. Lead designer Tom Wright answered the brief with designs of a hotel resembling a boat. Built out to sea on its own artificial island, it would definitely be a building to turn heads.

As can be seen from the exterior, the habitable floors stop quite a way before the tip of the structure. Nevertheless, it is still surprising to learn that a building of this size only has twenty-eight storeys, and a total of 202 bedroom suites. This is down to each floor being a double storey, just one of the signs of the opulence this building could afford. No expense was spared on the building's finishing touches either, as can be seen with the gold leaf, mosaics, and many types of marble used throughout. Often referred to as the world's only seven-star hotel, it's not hard to see why.

ATRIUM

The hotel's atrium is the biggest in the world, stretching from the lobby right up to the top floor. As it fills the space between the two wings, it also takes up a considerable one third of the space the building has to offer. In terms of volume it is 285 000 m³, the equivalent of 100 Olympic swimming pools.

BUILDING PLAN

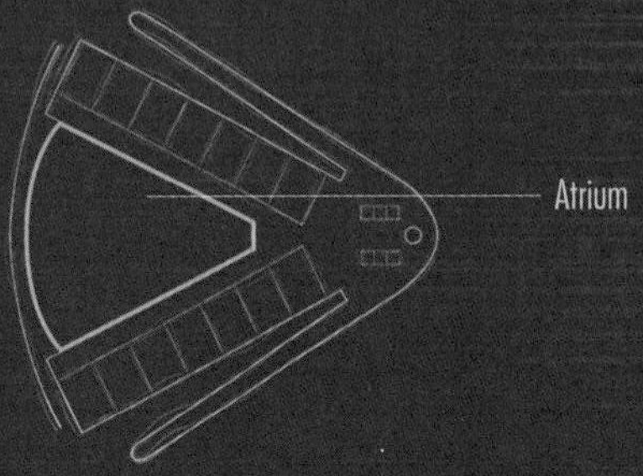

Atrium

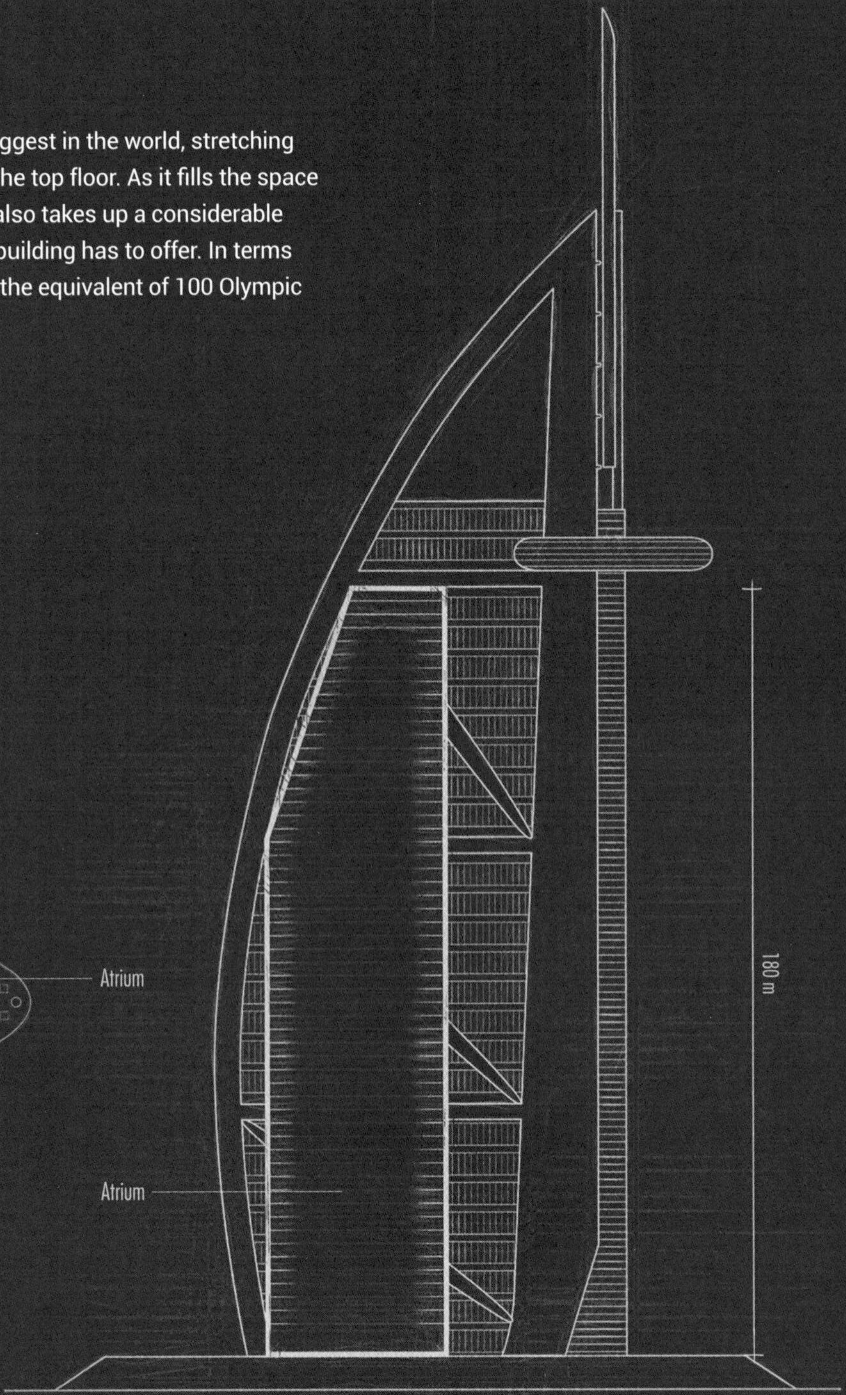

Atrium

180 m

HEAT GAIN

Due to the climate, buildings in this part of the world are particularly susceptible to heat gain. The greater the heat gain, the more expensive the running costs of the building will be, as more power will be used for air conditioning in order to counteract the amount of heat absorbed.

FABRIC SAIL

The broad end of the building is covered by a fabric that stretches across twelve curved sections supported by steel-trussed arches. During the day it appears clean and white, but at night it is backlit by coloured lights that change rhythmically throughout the night. The fabric is made from layered PTFE and fibreglass only 1 mm thick, and is good at dissipating heat, which helps to keep the building cool. In the daytime it allows light into the atrium by letting light diffuse through it, eliminating the need for conventional windows.

UNOCCUPIED HEIGHT

Adding a spire or pinnacle is a simple way of increasing the height of a skyscraper without costs escalating dramatically, or raising the complexity of the engineering involved. The Council on Tall Buildings and Urban Habitat refers to such parts of a building as 'vanity height' as they serve no practical purpose; they're just an excuse for the developers and property owners to show off. The practice is not new but it is the Burj Al Arab that exploits it the most – 39 per cent of the building's height is unoccupiable.

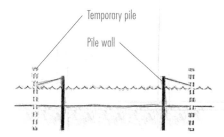

1 Sheet-pile walls that match the building's footprint were driven into the sand, supported by temporary piles.

BUILDING AN ISLAND

The island the Burj Al Arab sits on took a year to rise out of the sea. Situated 280 m from the shoreline it sits only 7 m proud of the water's surface which, although it may seem risky, creates the impression that the 'boat' is really sitting on the water. The island's perimeter is also lined with perforated concrete that acts like a sponge, and dampens the force of incoming waves.

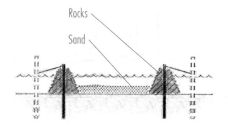

2 Rocks were piled up around the pile walls for support, and sand was used to fill in the middle.

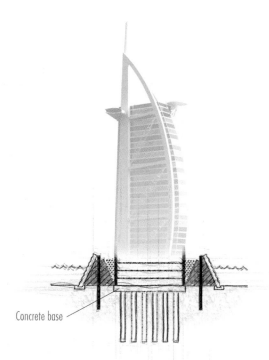

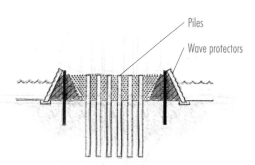

3 230 reinforced-concrete piles were driven 45 m into the seabed and the concrete wave protectors are positioned on the outside.

4 Some of the central sand was removed to expose the piles around which a concrete base was poured. The building of the main structure could then commence.

CONSTRUCTION:
1999–2004

HEIGHT:
509.2 м

TAIPEI
TAIWAN

TAIPEI 101

Taipei 101 has a record that can't be broken: to this day the tower is still the tallest building built in an earthquake zone, situated just 200 m from a major fault line. As the first building to reach half a kilometre in height, it marks itself out as a landmark building amongst landmark buildings.

As with other large building projects of the region, the design borrows heavily from eastern symbolism. As well as the number 8 making its appearance (most clearly in the 8 identical sections that make up the shaft), 101 is significant too. The number 101 has connections with the passing of time and new beginnings, for when writing New Year's Day numerically it appears 1-01 (1 January). Traditionally, 100 is associated with perfection and, by association, 101 is even better. In this case the number symbolises going beyond perfection and the pursuit of excellence. The 101 floors of the building are

therefore a direct link between the structure and the ideas of new beginnings and excellence.

However, the tower would need more than symbolism and signs of good fortune to survive its harsh environment. As well as having to contend with earthquakes, the region is also a typhoon hotspot, making it far from geographically suitable for such a tall building. A combination of very deep foundations and a structure that would be flexible enough to resist structural damage, yet sturdy enough to remain comfortable for its inhabitants, was needed. The resulting tower, in the end, was designed to withstand an earthquake of magnitude 9.0.

Upon completion, architect C. P. Wang (from C. Y. Lee & Partners) who led the design, had not only succeeded in creating the world's tallest building but, quite remarkably, one of the world's most stable buildings.

TUNED MASS DAMPER

Since Taipei 101 was built so close to a fault line, extra precautions were taken to limit the effects of an earthquake. To help resist any movement of the building, a large steel pendulum, known as a tuned mass damper, was hung from the 91st floor down to the 87th, resting in hydraulic rams at its base. Should the building sway, the swing of the steel ball pulls against the motion of the building, therefore reducing the effects.

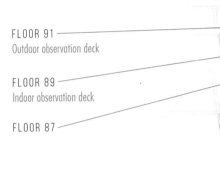

FLOOR 91
Outdoor observation deck

FLOOR 89
Indoor observation deck

FLOOR 87

STEEL SPHERE

The mass damper was the largest damper sphere in the world on completion. It consists of 41 circular steel plates welded together, each plate being 12.5 cm thick, to create a ball that weighs 660 tonnes.

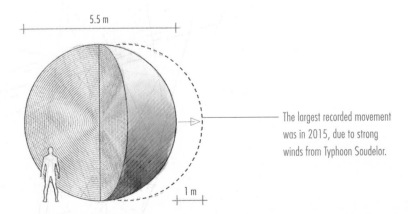

5.5 m

1 m

The largest recorded movement was in 2015, due to strong winds from Typhoon Soudelor.

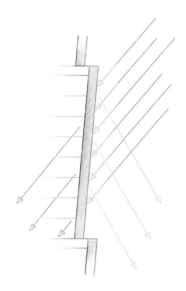

ENERGY EFFICIENT WINDOWS

The tower was designed to be energy-efficient – from the artificial lighting to the use of recycled water that accounts for about a quarter of the building's needs. The windows of the building are no exception. Made from double-glazed blue-green solar control glass, it offers excellent UV protection and blocks external heat by 50 per cent.

STRUCTURE

At the core of the building there are sixteen columns made from steel and eight steel super columns around the perimeter, two on each wall. For extra strength these columns are filled with concrete, but only up to floor 62; from then on the structure is steel only. Every 8th floor of the building is mechanical only, containing steel trusses that link the core to the perimeter.

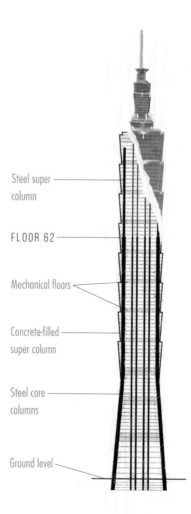

Steel super column

FLOOR 62

Mechanical floors

Concrete-filled super column

Steel core columns

Ground level

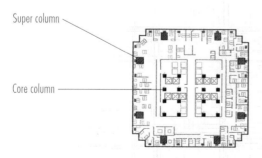

Super column

Core column

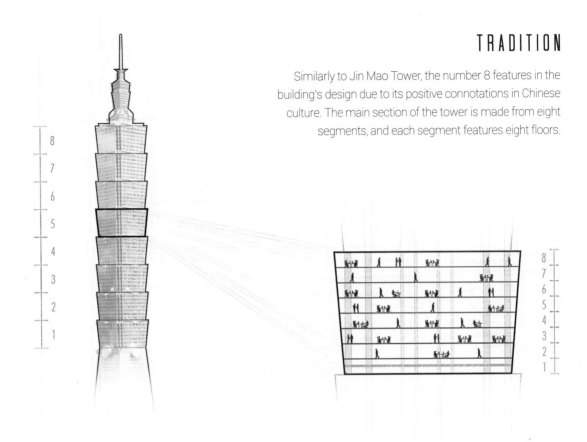

TRADITION

Similarly to Jin Mao Tower, the number 8 features in the building's design due to its positive connotations in Chinese culture. The main section of the tower is made from eight segments, and each segment features eight floors.

SYMBOLISM

The building emulates bamboo, as does the BOC Tower in Hong Kong, because of its ties with growth. It does, however, approach it from a different angle, choosing to focus on the notches along the edges rather than the angles created at the end.

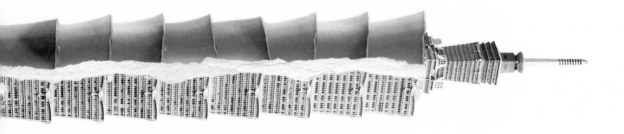

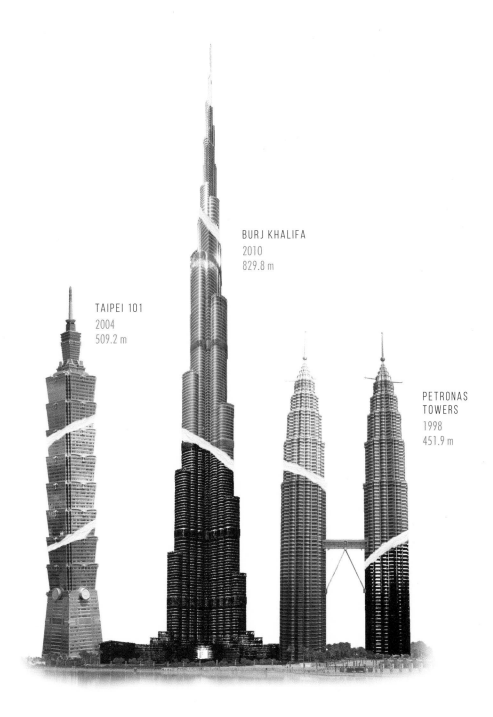

BURJ KHALIFA
2010
829.8 m

TAIPEI 101
2004
509.2 m

PETRONAS
TOWERS
1998
451.9 m

WORLD'S TALLEST BUILDING

Upon it's completion in 2004, Taipei 101 became the world's tallest building, holding
the title until the Burj Khalifa took it six years later.

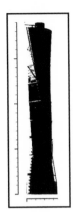

CONSTRUCTION:
2001–05

HEIGHT:
190.0 M

MALMÖ
SWEDEN

TURNING TORSO

The Turning Torso's remarkable design, the way it twists as it rises, marks it out as the first of its kind. It's the brainchild of Santiago Calatrava, a multifaceted Spanish designer experienced in painting, architecture, structural engineering and sculpture, who is particularly well known for creating innovative suspension bridges.

As far back as 1985, Calatrava was creating sculptures in his Torso series, that featured cubes of white marble stacked on top of one another and fastened together by a 'spinal column'. As they rise, each cube rotates, with the top cube turned 90 degrees in relation to the base. The sculptures' arrangement hints at the form of a human spine; movement in nature, and the human body, were Calatrava's fundamental inspirations.

In 1999 Johnny Örbäck, then the managing director for the cooperative housing association HSB, approached Calatrava, having seen his sculptures, and propositioned him with creating a landmark for Malmö. Despite Örbäck's conviction that the building would be successful, Calatrava took some convincing. He wasn't so sure it would be workable; not only would turning his 1.5 m artwork into a high-rise structure definitely require modifications, but would the finished product retain the same sense of motion? A central core would have to run through the building to support the weight and house the elevators and stairs, and as a result the cubes would need to transform into irregular shapes to create floor space. Needless to say these ideas were pursued, and the resulting building is a close representation of the sculpture that inspired it.

NOVEL TWIST

The tower is clearly not one of the tallest structures on the planet, but because of its innovative design it is one of the more noteworthy tall buildings. Indeed, it was the first ever twisting high-rise building, a style that has now been copied the world over.

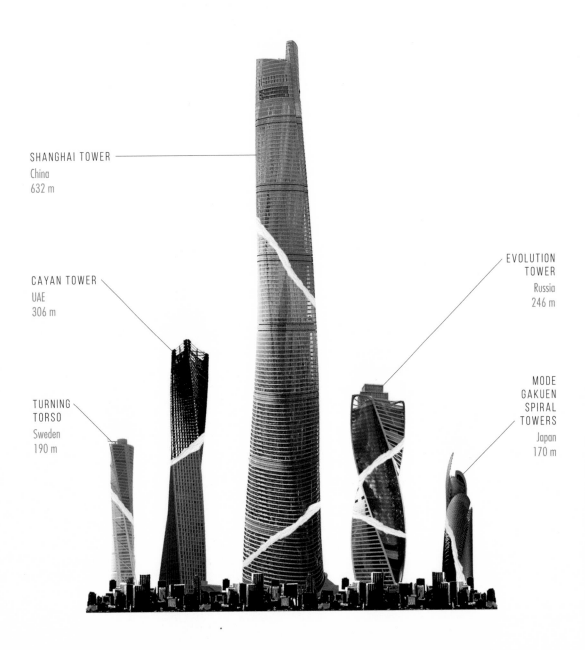

SHANGHAI TOWER
China
632 m

CAYAN TOWER
UAE
306 m

TURNING
TORSO
Sweden
190 m

EVOLUTION
TOWER
Russia
246 m

MODE
GAKUEN
SPIRAL
TOWERS
Japan
170 m

WONKY WINDOWS

Due to the building's twisted shape, the facades are not the usual vertical or flat surfaces. The Turning Torso's windows are irregular, shaped like parallelograms with straight horizontals and diagonal 'uprights', and also lean outward or into the building by up to 7 degrees.

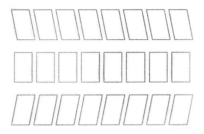

NEW SKYLINE

Since the 1970s Malmö's skyline had featured a giant crane that was used in the local shipyard. As the fixture, the Kockums Crane (Kockumskranen), was to be dismantled and transported to South Korea in 2002, local politicians thought it necessary that the skyline should not be left without a landmark.

190 m

138 m

STRUCTURE

The Turning Torso is composed of nine box units, with five floors within each unit. The floors are nearly square, with a triangle section added on one side, and each is rotated by 1.6 degrees, giving a nicely consistent twist to the building. Through the middle of the units rises a cylindrical concrete core that houses the elevators, staircase and services.

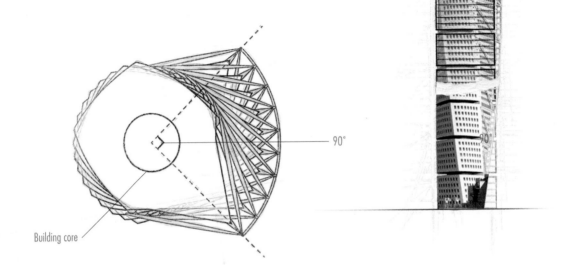

90°

Building core

SPINE

The tower's white-painted exterior steel structure that spirals upwards resembles a human spine, and transfers any lateral forces to the building core via the many horizontal and diagonal supports.

AUTOMATIC CLIMBING STRUCTURE

To ensure a fast building rate, the construction teams relied on an Automatic Climbing Structure (ACS). This machine fitted inside the central core and, with a crane-like arm sticking out the top, was able to pour concrete into moulds at the current working height. Once the concrete had hardened, the ACS would pull its way up and begin on the next floor. To keep it working, a concrete pump at ground level pumped concrete up to it, at a rate of 1 tonne per second.

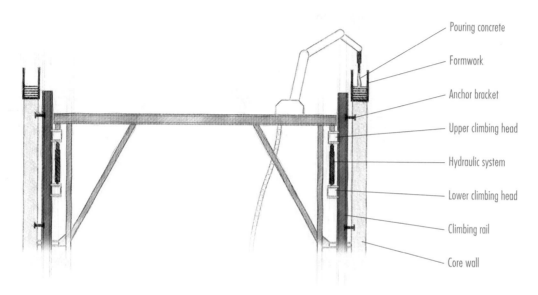

- Pouring concrete
- Formwork
- Anchor bracket
- Upper climbing head
- Hydraulic system
- Lower climbing head
- Climbing rail
- Core wall

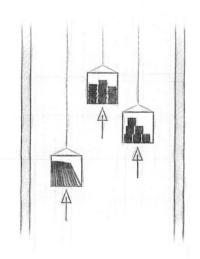

ELEVATED CONSTRUCTION

During construction, it was impossible to install hoists because of the curving facade. Instead, the elevators located inside the core were used to lift the construction materials, and therefore needed rebuilding as the structure rose.

CONSTRUCTION:
2002–05

HEIGHT:
322.5 M

QUEENSLAND
AUSTRALIA

Q1

Situated in Gold Coast in south-eastern Queensland, the Q1 soars above the rest. The city is home to more than 100 buildings over twenty storeys, so it is considerably built-up, but it retains an air of easy-going fun that's unusual in a city; it is in fact billed as the theme-park capital of Australia and is an extremely popular tourist destination. The vast majority of high-rises in the city are residential.

Q1 was conceived of in the year 2000 by Iranian-Australian businessman Soheil Abedian, whose Sunland Group designed, developed and built the project. As the Olympics had just taken place in Sydney they took inspiration from the Olympic torch for the building design, and as a nod to the nation's sculling team, Q1, they used the team name to brand the building.

Aside from towering over its neighbours, Q1 also stands out from the crowd due to its departure from the box-like norm of high-rises, and its slick glass-enclosed facade. Upon its completion towards the end of 2005 it became the tallest purely residential building in the world, and the tallest building in the Southern Hemisphere, although both titles have since been surpassed. It is, however, still Australia's tallest building.

ON THE ROOF

For those with a head for heights, Q1 offers an exhilarating walk in the sky. A high-speed elevator takes passengers to level 77 where they can, wearing a safety harness, climb out into the open air. Starting at about 240 m above ground level, participants make their way up a staircase, following the path of the oval-shaped roof structure. The highest accessible section is 30 m above the start point, allowing for unparalleled 360-degree views 270 m above the city streets.

138 m

GREENHOUSE

The apartments at Q1 share its 'Skygarden', a man-made rainforest featuring palms, trees and ferns, that thrives in the atrium of the building. Starting at level 60 and rising ten floors, the atrium allows room for plants up to 30 m tall. Being situated 180 m from the ground, it's surely one of Australia's biggest, highest greenhouses.

SOUTHERN HEMISPHERE'S TALLEST BUILDING

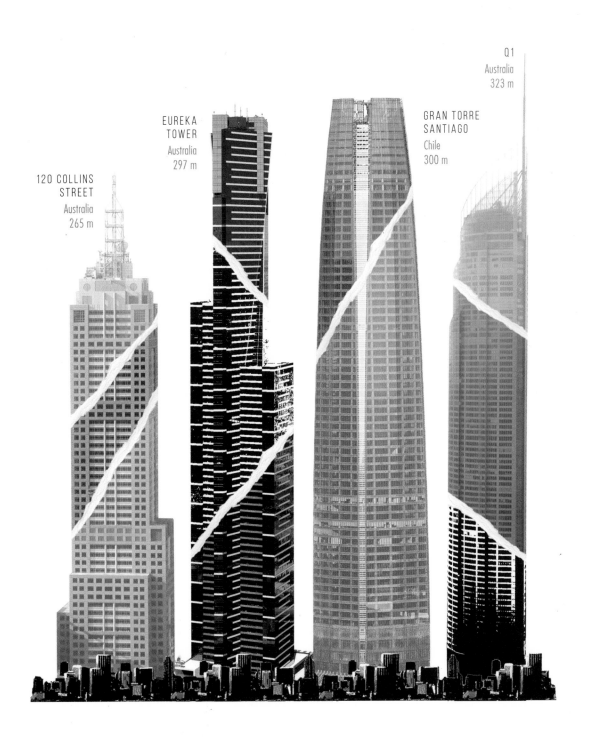

120 COLLINS
STREET
Australia
265 m

EUREKA
TOWER
Australia
297 m

GRAN TORRE
SANTIAGO
Chile
300 m

Q1
Australia
323 m

323 m

337 m

TALLEST RESIDENTIAL

When it was completed, Q1 became the tallest residential building in the world. It held on to this title from 2005 until 2011 when The Marina Torch opened.

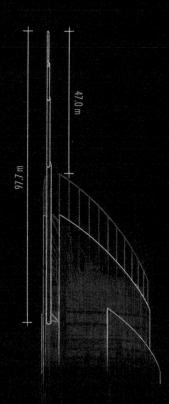

47.0 m

97.7 m

SPIRE

The spire that starts at level 75 reaches 47 m above the rest of the structure. Weighing a total of 87 tonnes, the 97.7 m structure was erected in 12 sections, making it one of the longest spires in the world.

NIGHT LIGHT

At night, powerful arc lights illuminate the spire so brightly that it can be seen from over 200 km away.

CONSTRUCTION:
1997 – 2008

HEIGHT:
494.3 m

SHANGHAI
CHINA

THE SHANGHAI WORLD FINANCIAL CENTER

The Shanghai World Financial Center (SWFC) was the second supertall to arise in the city's Pudong district. Despite the building's rather dry name, it is not solely an office building, but contains conference rooms, a museum, observation decks, retail space and a hotel that was the highest in the world when it was opened.

In 1997, the building's developers, Japan-based Mori Building Company, tasked skyscraper experts Kohn Pedersen Fox (KPF) with designing the world's tallest building in Shanghai's burgeoning financial district. The architects set to work creating the graceful, tapering form that we are familiar with, and at the building's top they included an aperture. On revealing their plans, locals objected to the tower's aperture and so the architects went away to reconfigure the design. It was at this time that C. Y. Lee's architectural firm began outlining their ideas for Taipei 101 in Taiwan, also aiming to create the world's tallest skyscraper.

Work on the SWFC's foundations began in August 1997, but construction then halted after their completion due to the Asian financial crisis. When work ceased, Mori used the opportunity to have the building redesigned so that it would beat Taipei 101 to first place. However, city planners capped the architectural height at 492 m, unfortunately dashing the hopes of the SWFC of it becoming the world's tallest. The new plans were, however, considerably taller than the foundations had been built for, and the new structure would have to be lighter and able to withstand greater wind loads due to the extra height. This was no easy feat, but the engineers were able to rise to the challenge, for which they have been highly praised, and work recommenced in 2004. It came in second place upon completion. Its roof and highest accessible floor are in fact higher than those of Taipei 101, as it's the spire that adorns the roof of the Taiwanese tower that awards it first prize.

FUNCTION AND STRUCTURE

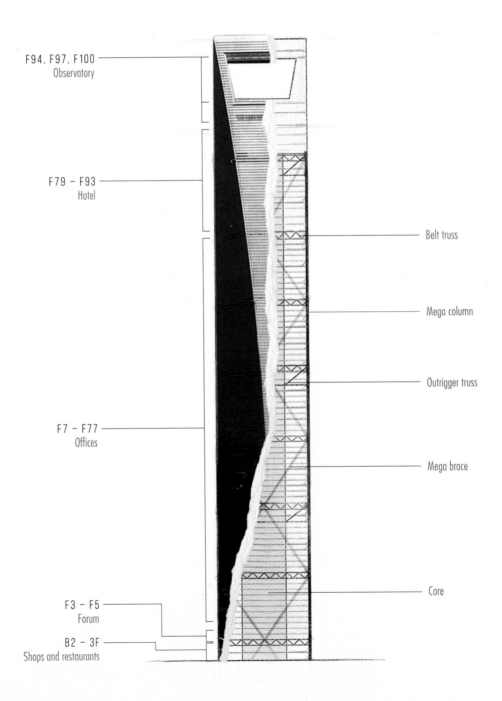

F94, F97, F100
Observatory

F79 – F93
Hotel

F7 – F77
Offices

F3 – F5
Forum

B2 – 3F
Shops and restaurants

Belt truss

Mega column

Outrigger truss

Mega brace

Core

OBSERVATION DECKS

The tower's three observation decks are positioned above and below the aperture. The lowest one is situated on the 94th floor. It features an 8 m high ceiling and, having the most floor space of the three, is sometimes used for exhibitions. The next deck is found on the 97th floor, immediately below the aperture, offering views of the sky through its glass ceiling. The highest observation deck runs along the top of the aperture; along with its floor-to-ceiling glass walls it also has a glass floor, providing a truly unique perspective of the city below.

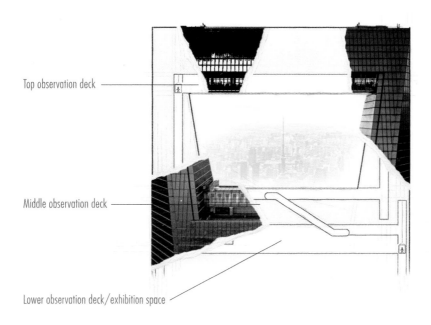

Top observation deck

Middle observation deck

Lower observation deck/exhibition space

NO SPIRE

The SWFC was the tallest flat-top building in the world when completed. It was planned to be 509 m tall so that it would steal the 'world's tallest' crown from Taipei 101, but the height restrictions that were imposed capped the roof at 492 m. Suggestions were made to add a spire to the building so that it could become the world no.1, but both the architect and developer were in agreement that it would damage the building's aesthetic.

ORIGINAL APERTURE

The aperture at the top of the building was included predominantly as a means of reducing stress on the building from the wind force. In initial designs it was circular, for in Chinese mythology the sky is often represented by a circle. It was modified to the trapezoid after locals complained it was too evocative of the Japanese flag's rising sun motif. The structure's final form is very reminiscent of a bottle opener.

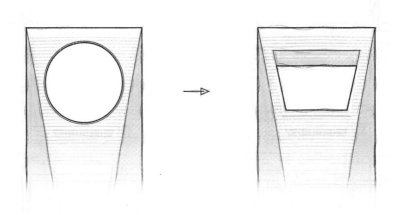

OTHER APERTURES

The SWFC is far from the only building to feature such a prominent aperture. Here are others from around the globe.

KINGDOM CENTRE
Saudi Arabia

DUKE ENERGY
CENTER
USA

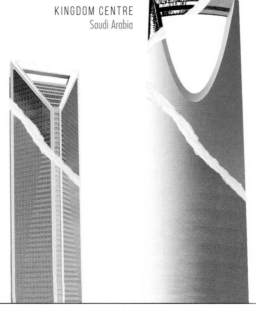

GUANGZHOU
CIRCLE
China

TALL AND SLENDER

As with many tall buildings, the SWFC tapers towards the top. The benefits of this sort of design have been exploited by skyscrapers the world over and include less weight to support, a lower centre of mass, and a reduction in forces from wind. The floor plans start as a square for the ground floor, gradually becoming more elongated as they go higher up the building.

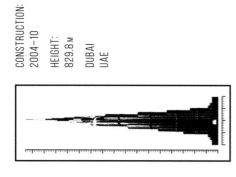

CONSTRUCTION:
2004–10

HEIGHT:
829.8 M

DUBAI
UAE

BURJ KHALIFA

The Burj Khalifa pierces the sky above it, penetrating the clouds. From the onset it was designed to be the tallest building in the world, soaring past its predecessor, Taipei 101, and the centrepiece of the booming financial and recreational hub of Dubai. It was the vision of the chairman of Emaar Properties, Mohamed Ali Alabbar, who wanted to see Dubai reap yet more international recognition for astonishing architecture.

To see the project through they chose Adrian Smith, who was then with Skidmore, Owings & Merrill, based on the quality of the designs he proposed. In the early stages, the building was only around 10 m taller than the reigning champion, Taipei 101. Ten metres is a fairly typical increment of growth for a succeeding 'world's tallest building', and has been as far back as the Chrysler Building. However, this was about to be turned on its head. Redesigns on the Burj Khalifa were to follow, but the final height was kept a closely guarded secret, lest any competitors attempt to beat it during the years it would take to construct. The finished height of the building was only revealed close to its completion, upon which it passed Taipei 101 by an astonishing 60 per cent. Not only that, it broke many other records by the time it was opened, including highest observation deck, building with most floors (211), highest occupied floor, highest elevator installation, highest vertical concrete pump and highest nightclub, to name but a few.

The Burj Khalifa has also won numerous awards for its breathtaking design, partly inspired by a desert flower, but largely, according to Smith, due to the amount of time it spent in the wind tunnel. The proportions of the setbacks that give the

USAGE

In the early stages of planning, the Burj Khalifa was intended to be entirely residential, but became mixed-use after the decision was made to include offices and other facilities.

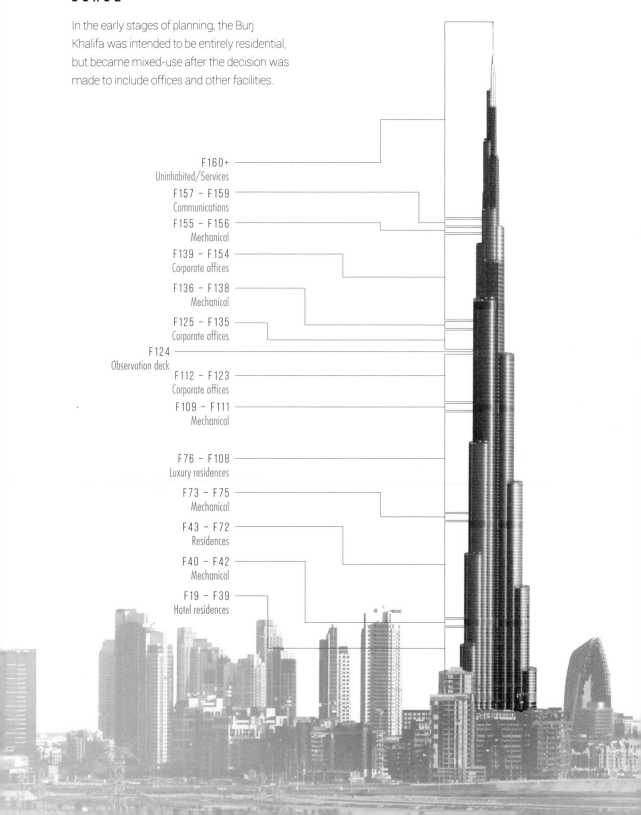

F160+
Uninhabited/Services

F157 – F159
Communications

F155 – F156
Mechanical

F139 – F154
Corporate offices

F136 – F138
Mechanical

F125 – F135
Corporate offices

F124
Observation deck

F112 – F123
Corporate offices

F109 – F111
Mechanical

F76 – F108
Luxury residences

F73 – F75
Mechanical

F43 – F72
Residences

F40 – F42
Mechanical

F19 – F39
Hotel residences

SPIDER LILY

The building's plan is an abstract representation of a Hymenocallis flower, and it creates a triple-lobed footprint. The flower, also known as the Spider Lily, is fragile and beautiful but resilient enough to cope with harsh climates and extreme temperatures — a fitting symbol for the building. When seen from above, the setbacks look quite petal-like.

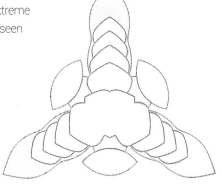

TALLEST STRUCTURE

The colossal building became not only the world's tallest, but also the world's tallest structure when it was completed. By surpassing the height of the CN Tower in Toronto, it became the first building since the Empire State to hold both titles simultaneously.

830 m

553 m

443 m

entire building its spire-like dimensions, proved themselves during testing, and result in minimising wind vortices that would rock the building back and forth. Not just elegant, but practical as well.

With the Burj Khalifa comes a new class of scraper known as megatall, the requirement of which is that the building is a minimum of 600 m tall. The Burj Khalifa sails past this. It's fitting that a building as exceptional as this should usher in a new era of construction.

FOUNDATIONS

The 450 000-tonne building is supported by a reinforced concrete raft that's shaped like the base of the building. This, in turn, is held up by 192 concrete piles, each measuring 1.5 m in diameter, and reaching over 50 m below ground level.

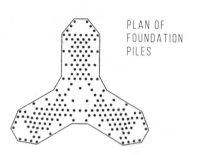

PLAN OF
FOUNDATION
PILES

50 m

SPIRE

The height of the uninhabited spire could match that of some entire skyscrapers.

157 m

241 m

244 m

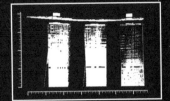

CONSTRUCTION:
2007 – 2010

HEIGHT:
206.9 M

DOWNTOWN CORE
SINGAPORE

MARINA BAY SANDS

The Marina Bay Sands is a jaw-dropping triumph of contemporary architecture and engineering. Its most impressive accomplishment is clearly the 2.5-acre park that sits on top of the towers, 200 m above the ground. Complete with swimming pools, jogging paths, gardens and other amenities, not to mention the enormous cantilevered section protruding from the north tower, it couldn't fail to impress.

The resort is one of two large-scale resorts conceived by the Singapore government to further their economic and tourism objectives. To bring about their vision they sought the services of architect Moshe Safdie, to design what was to become the most expensive stand-alone integrated resort property ever built. Safdie, known for his skills in integrating open green spaces into his work, was a good fit for the project, as Singapore's urban design strategy included the notion of the 'garden city'. His inspiration for the fifty-five-storey, three-hotel towers that support the park was a deck of cards, very fitting for a recreational resort and especially one that contains such a well-equipped casino.

The Marina Bay Sands was planned to open in full in 2009, but due to labour shortages, escalating costs and the global financial crisis, construction was delayed. To draw in some revenue before the whole site was completed, the resort was opened in stages, with the first being in April 2010. The grand opening would not be until February 2011, although to see the immense project complete it was worth the wait.

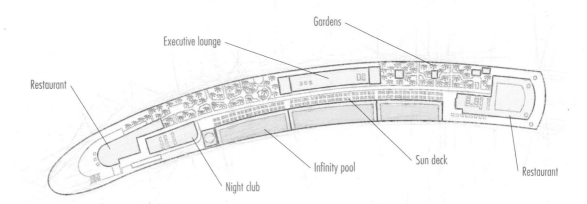

SKYPARK

The 12 400 m² Skypark on the roof bridges the gaps between the towers, as well as forming a cantilevered observation deck that juts out past the north tower. For the hotel guests there are many luxurious amenities, including a 146-metre-long infinity pool (split into three sections) as well as hundreds of trees and plants. At full capacity it can hold 3 900 people, and if stood on end it would surpass the height of the Chrysler Building.

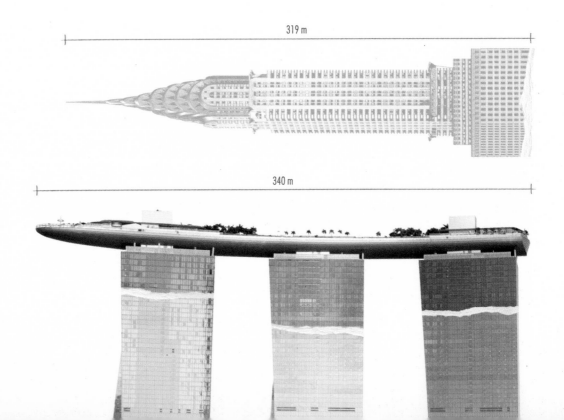

SKYPARK CONSTRUCTION

So that the skypark could become a reality, 7000 tonnes of structural steel needed to be assembled on the three towers' roofs. Sections of the structure were prefabricated on the ground and hoisted up to the roof by the lifting equipment mounted there. Pulling them upwards at a speed of 15 metres per hour, each of the steel sections took thirteen hours to reach the top.

HOISTING PROCEDURE

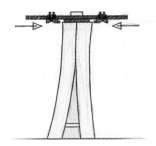

1 The steel structure is attached to the strand jack's cables, which measure 90 mm in diameter. The strand jack then lifts the structure steadily to the roof.

2 Jacks pull the steel structure in towards the building, holding the pieces above their final positions.

3 The segments are then lowered into place and bolted together. The whole process took about three days.

CANTILEVER CONSTRUCTION

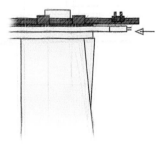

1 A sliding gantry extends out over the edge of the building.

2 A segment of the observation deck is attached to the cables and pulled up the building.

3 At the top, the segment is connected to the previous piece. When affixed, the sliding gantry extends again to repeat the process.

HOUSE OF CARDS

The sloping splayed walls of the towers created complicated challenges for the structural engineers, especially in the early stages of construction when the incline was at its most severe. Also to take into consideration was the extra force that the vertical wall would be under, as the sloping wall is, in effect, leaning on it. Each tower's legs join at level 23, creating a united floor plan, yet are stand-alone structures only linked by the Skypark on the roof. The design stems from Safdie's inspiration for the towers – a deck of cards.

MONEY MAKER

The giant complex contains a 2 561-room hotel split across the three towers, 250 meeting rooms, convention centre, world's largest atrium casino, two theatres, seven celebrity-chef restaurants and an ice-skating rink, among other amenities, and has become a highly profitable enterprise. This one site contributes upwards of 1.5 per cent of Singapore's GDP.

GAME ON

The atrium casino at Marina Bay Sands is well equipped.
It has 500 tables and 1 600 slot machines.

❖ Card table
▦ Slot machine

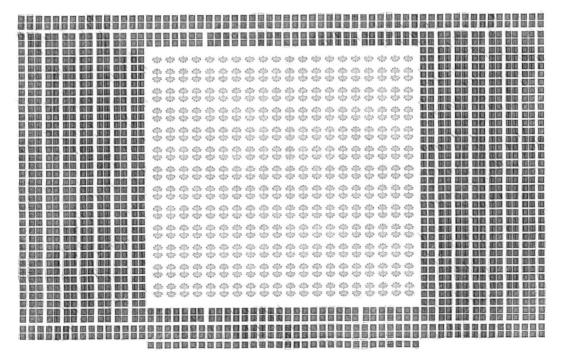

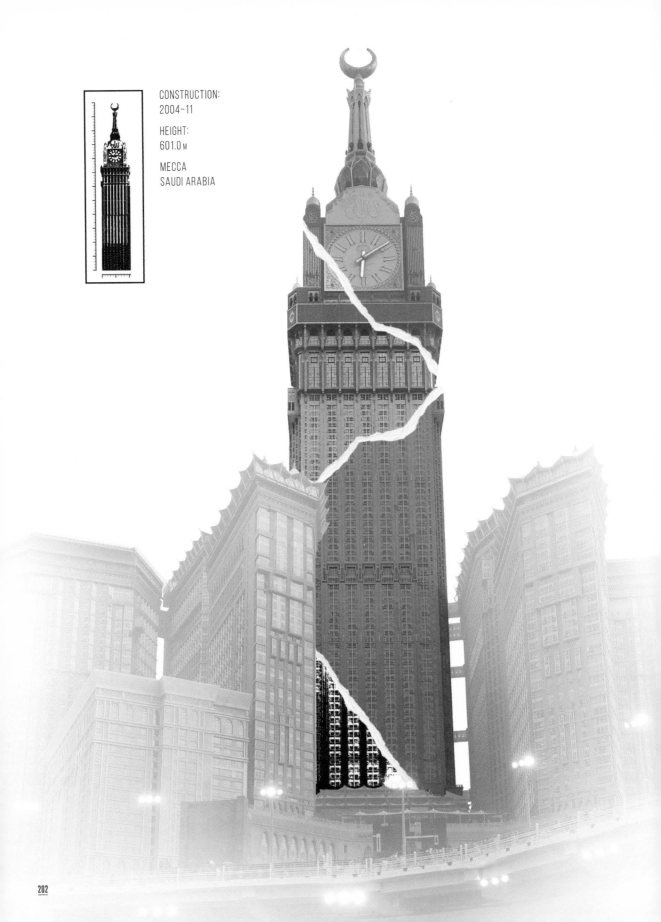

CONSTRUCTION:
2004–11

HEIGHT:
601.0 m

MECCA
SAUDI ARABIA

MAKKAH ROYAL CLOCK TOWER

The Makkah Royal Clock Tower is a truly mighty structure. It is the largest of a complex of seven skyscrapers that are situated right next to the Great Mosque of Makkah (transliterated to Mecca in English), the world's largest mosque and Islam's most sacred site. It is because of the holy site that this cluster of hotel buildings, collectively known as Abraj Al Bait, was created.

Islam requires every able Muslim to travel to Mecca at least once in their lifetime. The Hajj, as it is known, is an ancient pilgrimage in which participants enter the Great Mosque and circle the sacred Kaaba at its centre seven times. The event takes place over a five- to six-day period, and in 2017 more than 2 million people made the journey – a number that is ever increasing. To cater for such large hordes of people, and as part of the larger Saudi drive to diversify its economy, the Abraj Al Bait (the

Towers of the House) complex was built, which is now home to a convention centre, two heliports, a 4000-shop mega-mall, two large prayer rooms (one for men, one for women) able to hold over 10 000 people, and of course the 120-storey, five-star hotel in the main tower. It is at the top of this tower that the four largest clock faces in the world are set, their prominence justified by their duty to broadcast Islam's five daily prayer times. The clock faces can be seen from as far away as 30 km, and to signal prayer time thousands of white and green lights, the same colours as the Saudi flag, illuminate.

Designed by multidisciplinary firm Dar Group, headquartered in Beirut, the colossal structure caused controversy before the first stone was even laid. To make way for the behemoth, a historic 18th-century Ottoman fortress, called Ajyad Fortress, had to be destroyed.

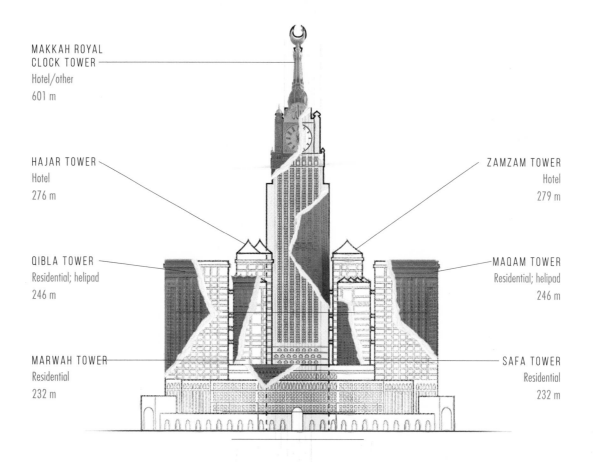

MAKKAH ROYAL
CLOCK TOWER
Hotel/other
601 m

HAJAR TOWER
Hotel
276 m

QIBLA TOWER
Residential; helipad
246 m

MARWAH TOWER
Residential
232 m

ZAMZAM TOWER
Hotel
279 m

MAQAM TOWER
Residential; helipad
246 m

SAFA TOWER
Residential
232 m

ABRAJ AL-BAIT

The Makkah Royal Clock Tower is the central structure in the
complex of seven towers, all of which rest upon a fifteen-
storey podium that houses a grand retail area.

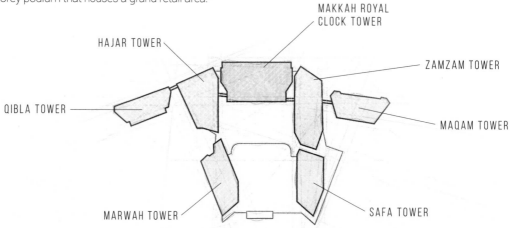

HAJAR TOWER

MAKKAH ROYAL
CLOCK TOWER

QIBLA TOWER

ZAMZAM TOWER

MAQAM TOWER

MARWAH TOWER

SAFA TOWER

GOLD CRESCENT

The crescent at the top of the tower is made from fibreglass and surfaced with shining mosaic gold. Hidden inside the crescent is a prayer room, the highest of its kind. As tall as a six-storey building, it weighs around 35 tonnes.

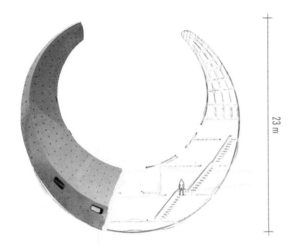

23 m

BULK

Although not the tallest building in the world, it has a larger amount of floor space. Including all seven buildings in the complex, the gross floor area is absolutely huge.

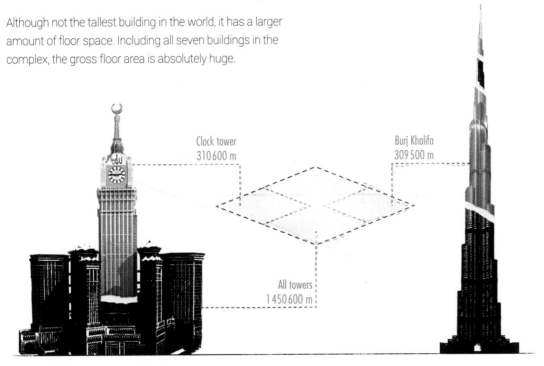

Clock tower
310 600 m

Burj Khalifa
309 500 m

All towers
1 450 600 m

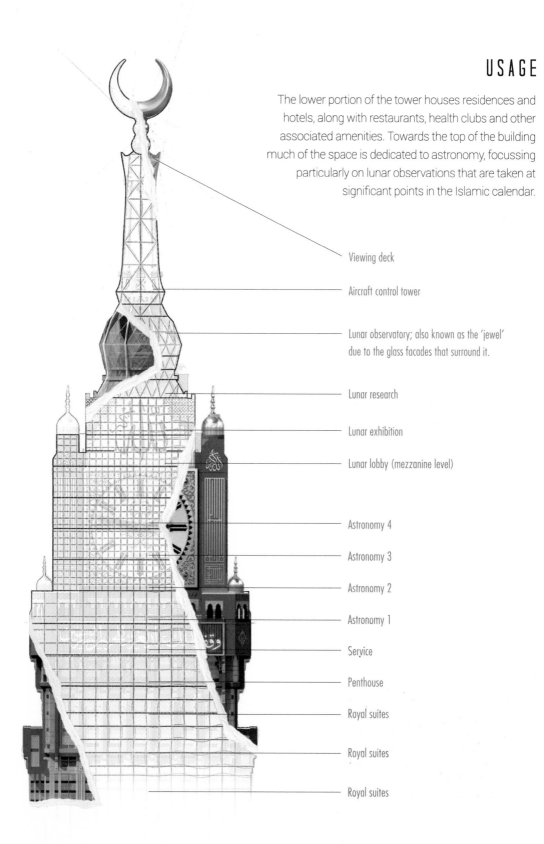

USAGE

The lower portion of the tower houses residences and hotels, along with restaurants, health clubs and other associated amenities. Towards the top of the building much of the space is dedicated to astronomy, focussing particularly on lunar observations that are taken at significant points in the Islamic calendar.

Viewing deck

Aircraft control tower

Lunar observatory; also known as the 'jewel' due to the glass facades that surround it.

Lunar research

Lunar exhibition

Lunar lobby (mezzanine level)

Astronomy 4

Astronomy 3

Astronomy 2

Astronomy 1

Service

Penthouse

Royal suites

Royal suites

Royal suites

HIGH TIME

The four clocks on the tower hold the record for being the highest
and the largest in the world.

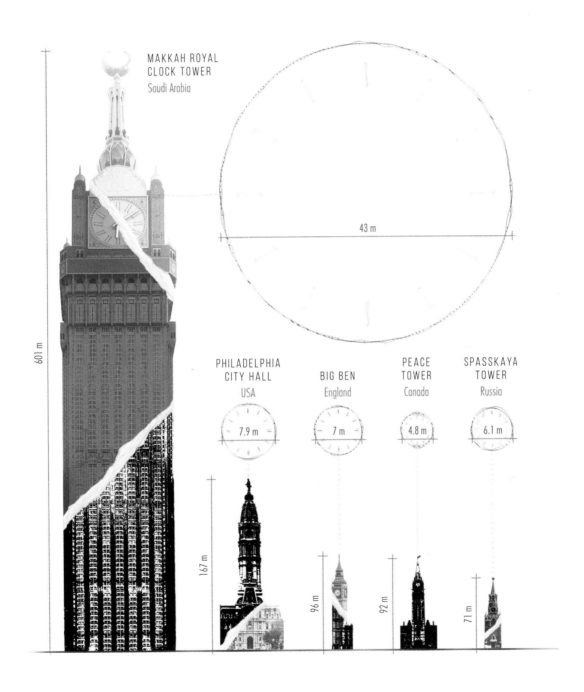

**MAKKAH ROYAL
CLOCK TOWER**
Saudi Arabia

601 m

43 m

**PHILADELPHIA
CITY HALL**
USA

7.9 m

167 m

BIG BEN
England

7 m

96 m

**PEACE
TOWER**
Canada

4.8 m

92 m

**SPASSKAYA
TOWER**
Russia

6.1 m

71 m

CONSTRUCTION:
2008-12

HEIGHT:
634.0 M

TOKYO
JAPAN

TOKYO SKYTREE

Skyscrapers are a somewhat recent phenomenon in Japan due, in part, to the severe earthquakes that affect the region. As a countermeasure, Japan's building laws stated that the height of a building could be no greater than 31 m, right up until 1963. A change in building regulations, coupled with a thriving post-war economy, lead to a building boom in Tokyo during the 1960s and 1970s.

Over the next few decades, even amid the rapid development of other Asian nations, Japan emerged with one of the strongest economies in the world. Construction in Tokyo continued steadily, with taller buildings emerging more frequently, and this had the adverse effect of interfering with television transmissions. The city's previous communications mast, Tokyo Tower, standing at 333 m tall, had been in operation since 1958, and no longer had the vantage point to transmit over the modern skyline. Thus, the city's six large TV broadcaster corporations

deemed it necessary to construct a new tower of at least 600 m to restore the service. In 2005 the rights to develop the tower were awarded to the Tobu Railway Corporation who, in turn, used the architectural firm Nikken Sekkei – the team behind the original Tokyo Tower.

The secondary aim of the developers was to create a monumental tourist attraction. Contrary to the Tokyo Tower, the objective was to create a structure that captured the essence of Japan, something that harnessed beauty as well as technical innovation. To that end, Tokyo Skytree is an unbridled success, as well as becoming the tallest tower in the world to boot.

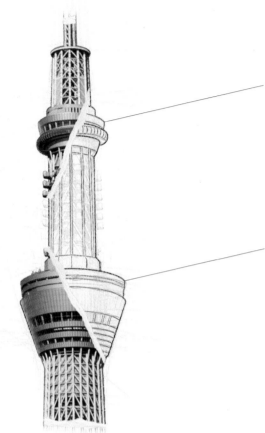

OBSERVATION DECKS

TEMBO GALLERIA

The two-tiered Tembo Galleria observation deck is the highest in the building.

The tiers of this observation deck are 5 m apart and are linked by a spiralling, tubular corridor that wraps around the structure's edge. The corridor has a shallow gradient and its steel and glass construct immerses visitors in the sky.

TEMBO DECK

The top level has the largest windows, providing the best panoramic views from the Tembo Deck. There is also a cafe, and ticket office for the Tembo Galleria.

The middle level contains a gift shop and restaurant.

On the lower level there is another cafe, and glass-floored areas where visitors can see directly down to the tower base.

BROADCASTING

The Tokyo Skytree's antenna provides television and radio broadcasting for the Greater Tokyo Area and beyond. It replaced Tokyo Tower, built in 1958, as the primary broadcast tower because Tokyo Tower's signal became impaired as high-rises were built up around it.

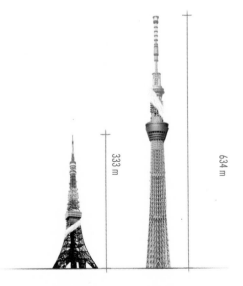

333 m

634 m

CROSS-SECTION

The base of the building is tripod-like at its base; its cross-section is perfectly triangular. As the height increases, the corners are softened and the cross-sectional shape becomes more circular. At 300 m the shaft of the building is cylindrical.

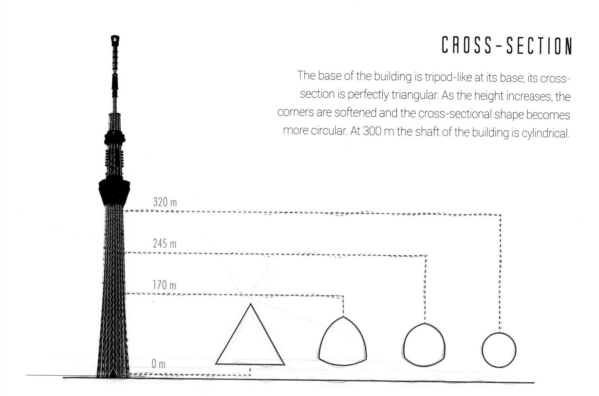

DAMPERS

To combat the effects of the earthquakes that the region is prone to, the outer structure is only rigidly attached to the central core for the first 125 m. From there on, until 375 m, the fixed welded beams are replaced by hydraulic dampers that cushion the effects of a violent shaking.

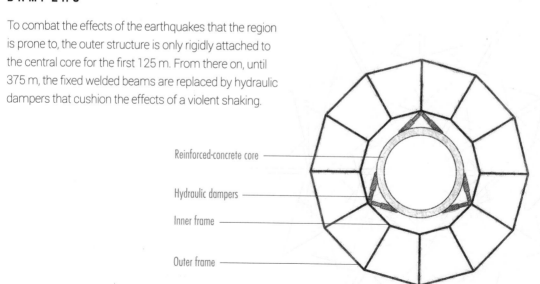

Reinforced-concrete core

Hydraulic dampers

Inner frame

Outer frame

WORLD'S TALLEST TOWERS

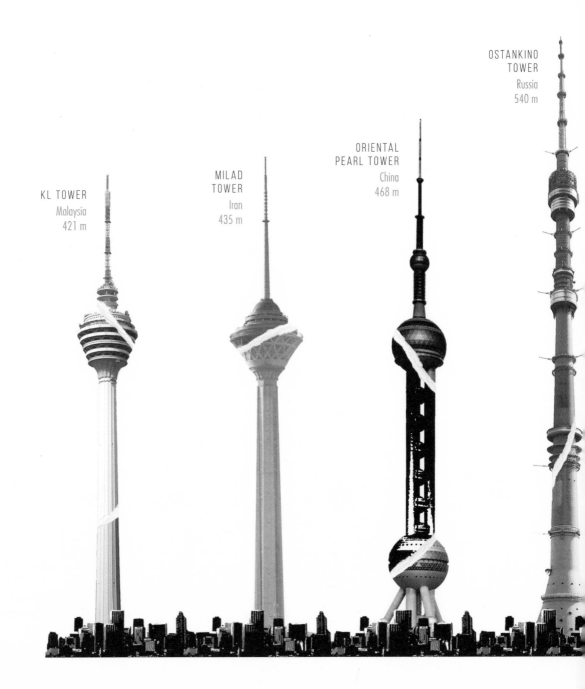

OSTANKINO
TOWER
Russia
540 m

ORIENTAL
PEARL TOWER
China
468 m

MILAD
TOWER
Iran
435 m

KL TOWER
Malaysia
421 m

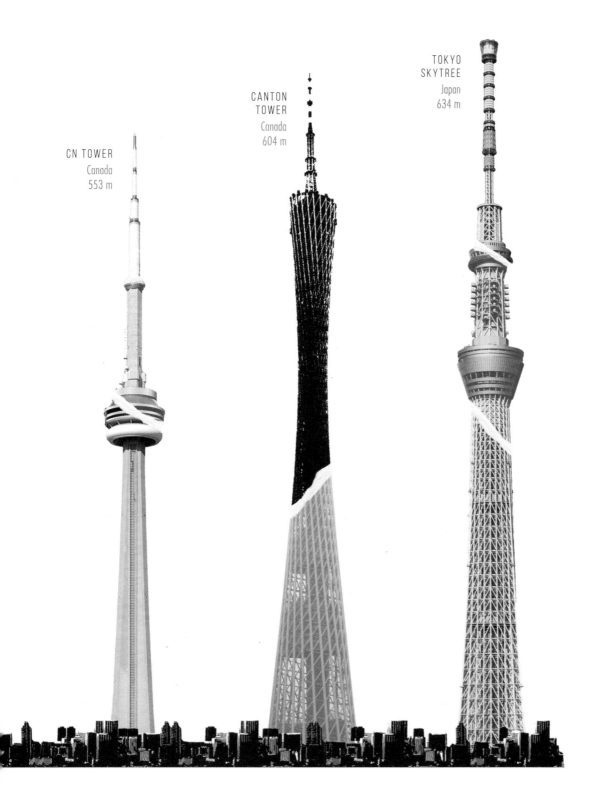

CN TOWER
Canada
553 m

CANTON
TOWER
Canada
604 m

TOKYO
SKYTREE
Japan
634 m

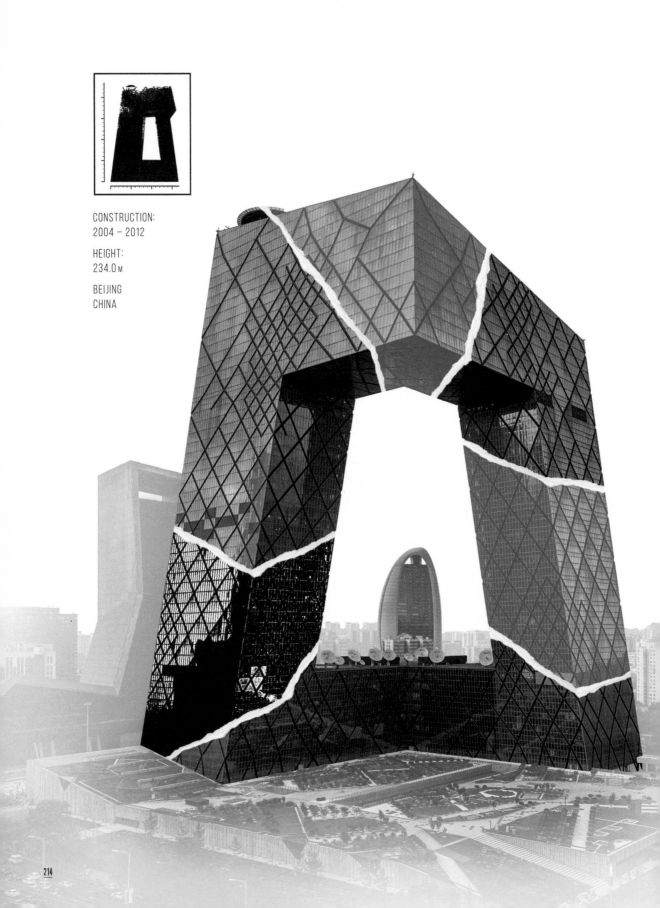

CONSTRUCTION:
2004 – 2012

HEIGHT:
234.0 M

BEIJING
CHINA

CCTV Headquarters

The Chinese Central Television (CCTV) Headquarters is an enigma to behold; its gravity-defying form looks poised to topple at any given moment. Its evidently ingenious design, not just because of its implausible shape but also because of its daring to break free from conformity, has meant it has become a truly memorable building. One could argue that competing in the race for ultimate height is hopeless, as ruling the skyline can only be achieved for so long before another, even taller, building emerges. CCTV Headquarters bucks the trend and avoids falling into this trap by changing our perspective on what a skyscraper can be.

In 2002, the rapidly expanding state-run CCTV had plans to create more channels and move into the global market. In order to sustain the company's expansion, they held an international design competition for a new headquarters, which was won by the Office of Metropolitan Architecture (OMA). Their winning design sought to consolidate the operations within the building into a continuous loop of activities. Traditionally, the TV industry segregates its component functions, with administration and management in the financial district, production studios in industrial parts of town, and creative departments located in 'hip' areas. Inside the new headquarters everything would be under the same roof, and OMA envisaged that the continuous flow of the building's loop would promote social integration and unity within.

Although the height of the CCTV Headquarters is well within building-code limits, the Chinese government organised an expert panel of engineers to assess whether the unwieldly building was indeed safe. They focused mainly on its resistance to seismic activity and, using scaled down versions of the structure, devised numerous practical tests to analyse this. Satisfied with the design, construction was allowed to proceed, with the two towers built independently from one another before being joined by the overhanging cantilever.

FUNCTION

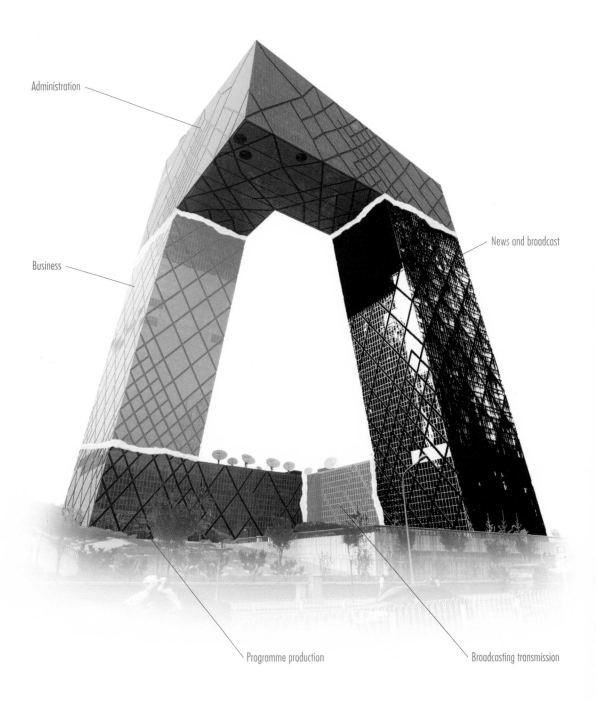

Administration

Business

News and broadcast

Programme production

Broadcasting transmission

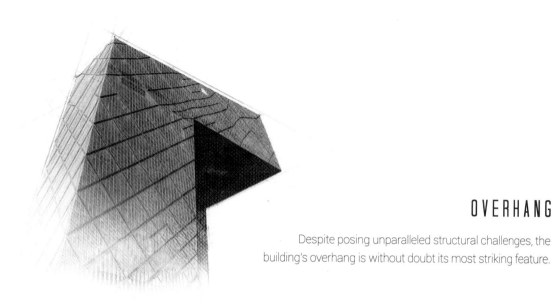

OVERHANG

Despite posing unparalleled structural challenges, the building's overhang is without doubt its most striking feature.

ABSTRACTED PYRAMID

As the building's plot is square, and all the exterior walls slope inwards by 6 degrees, it would fit flushly inside the confines of a pyramid. This helps with the stability of the building, for if the walls were all perpendicular, the overhang would be much weightier.

 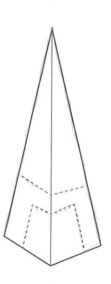 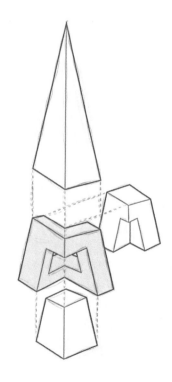

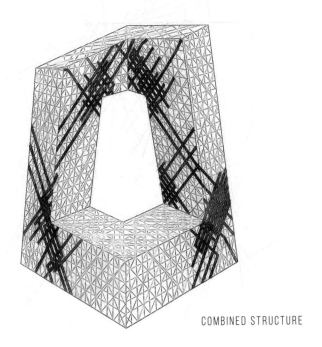

COMBINED STRUCTURE

DIAGRID STRUCTURE

Engineers decided early on that the only way the building's overhang would be strong enough is if the tube of the outer structure wrapped around every facade of the building. Preliminary designs were based on regularly spaced perimeter columns, beams and braces, but analysis of this structure showed that forces varied wildly across its different areas. In response to this the diagonal steel structure, known as a diagrid, was doubled-up in areas where extra strength and stiffness was required, and removed in other areas where flexibility was needed. This is expressed clearly on the building's facade, where the diagonal pattern doubles or halves in different areas.

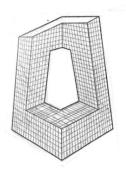

BASE STRUCTURE

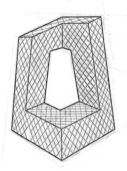

DIAGRID STRUCTURE

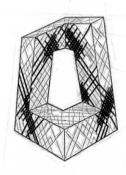

STRESS DISTRIBUTION
STRUCTURE

CONCRETE CORES

The building uses concrete columns of various sizes throughout the interior structure, that transfer loads to the ground. The elevators are also located inside vertical concrete load-bearing sections that act as the building's rigid cores. Unsurprisingly, due to the building's shape, these cores are not symmetrical, centrally located features.

SIZE ISN'T EVERYTHING

Since the dawn of skyscrapers over 100 years ago, technologies may have improved but the overall goal has been the same: to become the tallest. This is a building that deviates from that tradition, instead deriving its wow-factor from its impossible-seeming shape.

BURJ KHALIFA
830 m

SHANGHAI TOWER
632 m

LOTTE WORLD TOWER
555 m

ONE WTC
541 m

CCTV
HEADQUARTERS
234 m

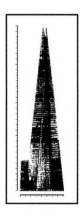

CONSTRUCTION:
2009–12

HEIGHT:
309.6 M

LONDON
ENGLAND

THE SHARD

The Shard began with the vision of Irvine Sellar, a British property developer who wanted to create a 'vertical city' in the heart of London. It was to incorporate retail space, offices, a hotel, apartments, restaurants and a public viewing gallery – and be architecturally striking. His idea was to create a structure that housed a dynamic, diverse community that could enjoy marvellous views of the city, whilst also experiencing the majesty of the building itself.

In early 2000, Sellar had lunch with Italian architect Renzo Piano, who was initially not convinced by the project, saying: 'I hate tall buildings – they are arrogant, aggressive, like fortresses.' He was, however, drawn to the energy of the nearby railway lines and the beauty of the river Thames. On the back of his menu he quickly sketched a spire-like sculpture emerging from the river. He had a vision for it to be light and transparent, in spite of its height; its elegance would be a

contrast to the bulky high-rises of old. When he saw the sketch, Sellar signed him up straight away.

Demolition of the twenty-five-storey Southwark Towers, which occupied the site, began in September 2007, and a year later the building was erased from the skyline. During this period, uncertainty in the global financial markets cast a shadow over the Shard's future, as investors got cold feet. Fortunately, Sellar was able to secure further funding from a consortium of Qatari investors, and the project was back on track. Construction began in March 2009 and the Shard's core exceeded 235 m by the end of November 2010, ending the eighteen-year reign of One Canada Square as Britain's tallest building. Upon completion in July 2012, the Shard became the tallest building in Europe, if only fleetingly. For in November that year it was surpassed by Moscow's Mercury City Tower.

GLASS 'SPLINTERS'

The Shard is made from eight splinters of glass that surround
the facade of the building. Beneath the splinters, but on the
outside of the internal glazing, automated blinds operate to
keep the building cool, reducing the energy consumption
incurred with air conditioning.

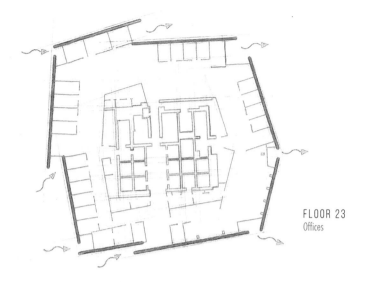

FLOOR 23
Offices

AIR FLOW

The splinters of glass themselves do not meet, as can be seen on the floor plan, allowing for natural air flow through the ventilation ducts. At the building's pinnacle there is a radiator designed to disperse heat from its core, adding to the building's environmentally friendly credentials.

SOLITARY SPIRE

Planning permission has traditionally not been granted in this area of London for such tall buildings. However, as the design was of exceptional quality, and after approval by public inquiry, it was deemed it wouldn't spoil views of the historic city.

TOP-DOWN CONSTRUCTION

In normal circumstances buildings are, predictably, built from the ground up. That is to say an area is excavated, foundations are driven into place, and work commences with the basement levels and proceeds to the ground level and so on. In an effort to cut time and costs the Shard used an innovative technique known as top-down construction, which allowed for the first twenty-three floors of the concrete core and some of the surrounding structure to be built before the basement had been fully excavated. Although the top-down technique had been used before, it was a world-first for such a tall building.

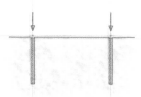

1 Retaining walls made of concrete are inserted into the ground, enclosing the site. This prevents subsidence in the surrounding earth.

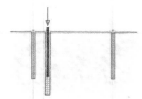

2 Concrete piles are driven into the ground and plunge columns of steel are set into them.

3 With enough piles in place, a concrete slab is then created at ground level that provides a stable base on which work above ground can commence.

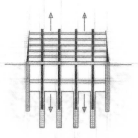

4 The building grows vertically, during which time excavation takes place below ground.

5 The basement and foundations are complete once the whole area is excavated and all the floors are in place above the original piles.

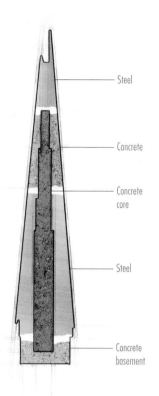

Steel

Concrete

Concrete
core

Steel

Concrete
basement

STRUCTURAL MATERIAL

The structure derives its stability from the massive concrete core that runs through the middle of the building, although the concrete and steel structures around it are layered like a trifle. It was designed like this due to the functionality of different areas of the building. For example, in residential areas concrete is preferred as it is a better acoustic insulator, whereas in office areas steel is favoured as it is easier to run power cables and the other services through it.

REFLECTED LIGHT

A traditional building with vertical walls reflects and scatters proportionally less light from the sky. The sloping walls of the Shard are made from extra-white glass and make the tower especially sensitive to the sky around it. The Shard's colour and mood is in a constant state of change with the time of day, weather and seasons.

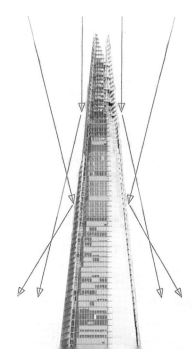

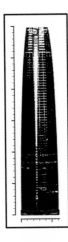

CONSTRUCTION:
2006–13

HEIGHT:
300.0 m

SANTIAGO
CHILE

GRAN TORRE SANTIAGO

The sixty-four-storey Gran Torre Santiago is a giant that overwhelms the city's other skyscrapers. The tallest building in Latin America, its height even competes with some of the hills of the Andean mountains, which provide the beautiful backdrop to Santiago. The tower is part of a larger complex that includes the largest shopping mall in South America, two hotels and two office towers.

Given the fact that Chile undergoes some of the most intense earthquakes on the planet, the design and engineering of the project would take considerable expertise. Horst Paulmann, billionaire CEO of giant retail firm Cencosud SA, hired César Pelli (of the Petronas Towers) to design what would become a universal point of reference in the city of 6 million people. Pelli approached the challenge head-on, creating a truly modern,

both technically and aesthetically, 21st-century building. It encompasses state-of-the-art structural and mechanical systems, including a highly advanced outrigger system to deal with the area's excessive seismic activity, and the cooling tower draws its whole water supply from the adjacent canal.

The global financial crisis impacted the progress of the Gran Torre Santiago, as it did the Shard, but this time during the construction phase. Work was halted for ten months in 2009, and the unfinished structure loomed over the city as a symbol of Santiago's shattered dreams of economic grandeur. This changed, however, when work restarted, with the tower signifying Chile's financial recovery.

FORM AND STRUCTURE

The building's form is relatively simple, but it has a few nice touches that elevate the design into something quite elegant. The building plan is basically a square whose sides bulge outwards, causing the walls that extend up from it to curve and reflect light in a more interesting fashion than if they were flat. The four sides of the building do not meet, but leave a gap in which recessed glass walls sit at 45 degrees to the main facades. Part way up the building the floor plan starts to shrink as the walls taper inwards, with each glass facade also becoming narrower, exposing more of the angled corners.

RECESSED CORNER

BUILDING PLAN

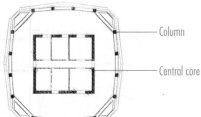

Column

Central core

The way the four walls seem detached from the building is emphasised by the open-topped latticed crown at the peak. In the centre of the building is its concrete core, slightly rectangular as opposed to square like the building's plan. Around the edge are sixteen reinforced-concrete columns, four along each wall, forming the outer section of the structure's tube.

TALLEST IN SOUTH AMERICA

The Gran Torre Santiago is the tallest building in South America, and the second tallest building in the Southern Hemisphere after Q1 in Australia.

GRAN TORRE SANTIAGO

Chile
300 m

ALVEAR TOWER

Argentina
241 m

PARQUE CENTRAL COMPLEX

Venezuela
255 m

BD BACATÁ

Columbia
246 m

TORRE COLPATRIA

Columbia
196 m

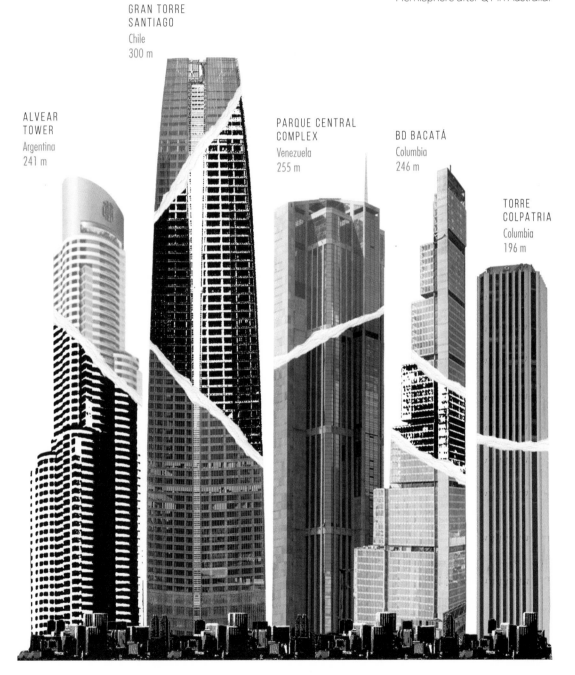

HIGH CEILINGS

Typically, floor-to-floor height in high-rise buildings is around 3 m, excluding the high ceilings of lobbies and atriums. This allows enough headroom and enough space to light and ventilate the interior, as well as enough space between ceiling and floor to house cables, pipes and air-conditioning ducts. The Gran Torre Santiago's floors are considerably further apart, allowing natural light to penetrate deeper into the building and create a more spacious feel to the interior.

4.1 m

3 m

GRAN TORRE
SANTIAGO

TYPICAL
SKYSCRAPER

FIRST ON THE SCENE

The tower dwarfs the other skyscrapers in the city as a symbol of the region's economic growth. It tops out at over 100 metres above Santiago's next tallest building.

EARTHQUAKE PROOF

The region experiences some of the harshest earthquakes on the planet; Chile in fact
currently holds the record for the highest recorded magnitude earthquake to date.
Gran Torre Santiago proved itself by withstanding an 8.8 magnitude earthquake on
27 February 2010, the twelfth-strongest earthquake ever recorded, without sustaining
damage. The earthquake is shown on the graph amongst the world's fifteen strongest.

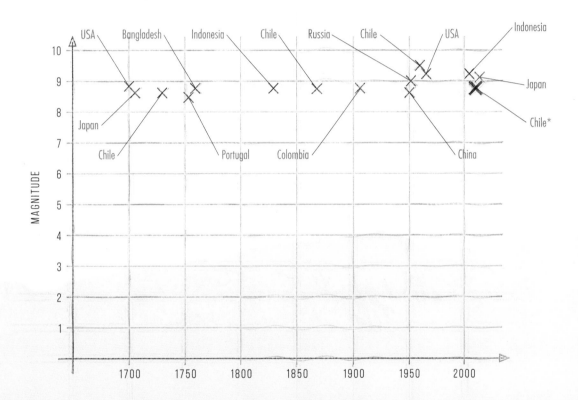

CONSTRUCTION:
2008-14

HEIGHT:
632.1m

SHANGHAI
CHINA

SHANGHAI TOWER

Shanghai Tower completes the set of three supertalls that were planned for Shanghai as far back as 1990 (along with Jin Mao Tower and the Shanghai World Financial Center), to transform what was previously farmland into the fastest-growing financial centre in Asia. Actually classified as megatall, it is the tallest of the three, and its vision of the 'vertical city' may well be a prototype for skyscrapers of the future.

The international firm Gensler won a competition for Shanghai Tower in 2007, with design concepts that focused on sustainability and community. The building is comprised of nine segments, each twelve to fifteen storeys high, that are stacked upon one another. On the bottom floor of each segment are atriums that contain gardens, cafes, restaurants and retail space, all of which are enclosed behind the twisting outer facade. The inspiration for the design came from traditional small-scale courtyards that are found in Shanghai, however in this instance the communities would not be living side by side, but on

top of each other. Environmentally, the outer facade that wraps around the inner structure and courtyards is greatly beneficial. By creating a blanket of air between itself and the building inside, it acts as an insulator, reducing energy consumption and bills.

As with the Burj Khalifa, its exterior aesthetics owe a lot to practicality, with extensive testing being carried out on models in the wind tunnel. The rotation of the glass facade, combined with the notch that runs the height of the tower, has the effect of slowing wind currents that can accumulate around the building, thus reducing structural loads.

The Shanghai Tower's innovative design is indeed practical and elegant. A tall building that provides amenities at regular increments, so that its occupants don't have to travel all the way to ground level for a loaf of bread, is surely the way forward. Time will tell if this catches on.

STRUCTURE

Similar to the Turning Torso, Shanghai Tower is also made from nine vertical segments, stacked on top of each other. Unlike the Swedish building, the segments are not identical to each other, but get taller and narrower the higher up the building. Their floor plans are circular, wrapped around a grid-like central core that diminishes with height as loads on it are reduced. Just inside the floors' circular exterior there are eight evenly spaced super columns positioned in pairs, with individual diagonal columns positioned between each pair. The cylindrical glass exterior of the building is only its inner facade, however; outside of this is another glass facade that sweeps around the building, creating the turning effect. At the bottom of each of the building's segments outriggers attach to the exterior facade, providing open (but indoor) spaces featuring retail spaces, gardens, cafes and restaurants.

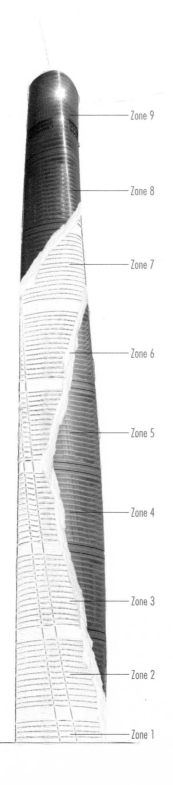

Zone 9
Zone 8
Zone 7
Zone 6
Zone 5
Zone 4
Zone 3
Zone 2
Zone 1

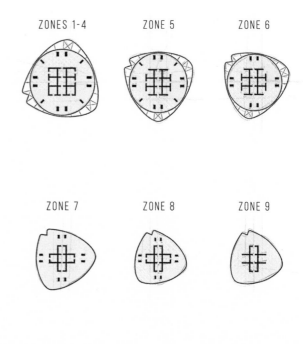

ZONES 1-4   ZONE 5   ZONE 6

ZONE 7   ZONE 8   ZONE 9

TWIN FACADES

Most buildings that have only one facade use highly reflective glass to counteract heat absorption. The double layer of glass on the Shanghai Tower eliminates the need for this, performing as a thermal insulator for the building, keeping it warm in winter and cool in summer. The twisting shape of the exterior facade, that turns by 120 degrees, also performs well in the wind, reducing wind force by 25 per cent compared to a conventional design. A reduction in wind force has meant less structural material was needed, reducing both the weight and cost of the project.

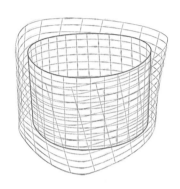

FOUNDATIONS

The tower sits on a hexagonal concrete raft on top of 947 piles, 1 m in diameter, that plunge down into the soft sandy earth. Beneath the load-bearing columns and core the formation of the piles is staggered, but in areas that take less stress they are laid out in a grid-like fashion. Below the core of the building the piles extend a little further as this area bears the brunt of the building's weight.

632 m

56 m

FOUNDATION PLAN

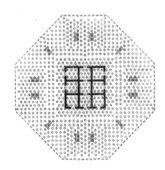

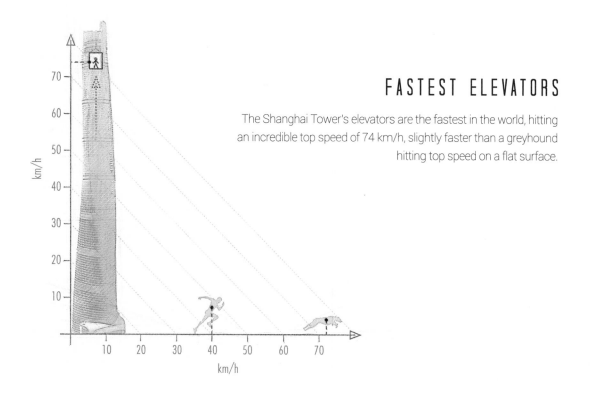

FASTEST ELEVATORS

The Shanghai Tower's elevators are the fastest in the world, hitting an incredible top speed of 74 km/h, slightly faster than a greyhound hitting top speed on a flat surface.

TOP FLOOR

Although second in total height to the Burj Khalifa, the Shanghai Tower's top floor is higher. It has little vanity height compared to the Burj Khalifa's massive spire.

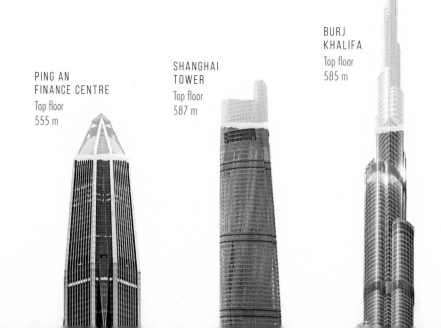

PING AN
FINANCE CENTRE
Top floor
555 m

SHANGHAI
TOWER
Top floor
587 m

BURJ
KHALIFA
Top floor
585 m

SUPERTALL CLUSTER

'Supertall' is a term that applies to skyscrapers over 300 m tall. Along with the Jin Mao Tower and the Shanghai World Financial Center, the arrival of the Shanghai Tower sets the Pudong District apart as having the only cluster of three supertalls in the world.

CONSTRUCTION:
2006–14

HEIGHT:
541.3 M

NEW YORK
USA

ONE WORLD TRADE CENTER

One World Trade Center rises monumentally above the New York skyline, symbolising the city's resilience in the aftermath of the worst terrorist attack the world has ever seen. The glass-clad megalith, while conveying a look of strength and permanence, also dazzles and amazes.

After a handful of uninspiring building plans were submitted following the original towers' demise, a competition was opened up by the Lower Manhattan Development Corporation, to determine how to use the site. Architect Daniel Libeskind won this, though his designs underwent many alterations – as site developer and leaseholder, Larry Silverstein, disagreed with his proposals. Silverstein brought David Childs, from the acclaimed Skidmore, Owings & Merrill, on board to steer the ship.

Understandably, safety was at the top of everyone's minds, and so Childs worked alongside terrorism experts to ensure that the building was one of the most robust on the planet. As a precaution he was advised to relocate the building further away from its adjacent road, to minimise threats from the street, and to further protect the building's base. Childs accomplished this by making it from windowless, reinforced-concrete walls that rise twenty storeys from the street, safeguarding the structure from truck bombs. The building has 91 cm thick concrete walls around all stairwells and elevator shafts, with extra sets of stairwells dedicated solely to firefighters, and the ventilation systems have filters to deal with biological and chemical threats. The list of safety features goes on, and with a strict new security protocol implemented at the site, the tower is as prepared as possible.

To top it off, the building's antenna reaches 541.3 m above ground, or 1776 feet. This is a nod to the year 1776, when the Declaration of Independence was signed.

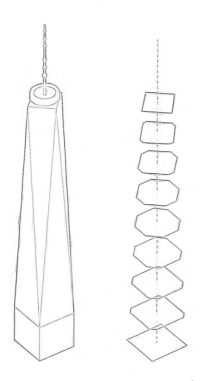

FORM

One World Trade Center rises from its cuboid base as the edges of the building slowly chamfer inward, thus creating eight elongated triangular facets on the building's surface. As a result, the floor plans start off square and become octagonal by mid-way up, and culminate in a square glass parapet on the roof, rotated 45 degrees from the base. The gently sloping geometric facades of the building catch the sun as it moves across the sky, scattering light and creating shapes like a kaleidoscope.

TALLEST IN NEW YORK

It was not only the tallest building in New York when completed, but the tallest in the US, and tallest in the Western Hemisphere. Shown here it is compared against its New York neighbours.

STRUCTURE

One World Trade Center is a hybrid concrete and steel structure. Unlike its predecessors, whose concrete cores were surrounded by an outer ring of steel columns, this building would derive more of its strength from its large, incredibly strong concrete core that uses a much lighter outer framework. The core is roughly square and reaches to the uppermost floors, diminishing as the building tapers. Steel beams set into the core, which is made from the strongest concrete used in New York to this point, support the floors, enabling vast column-free expanses. The steel framework around the edge of the building is ductile, for the absorption of lateral and seismic loads.

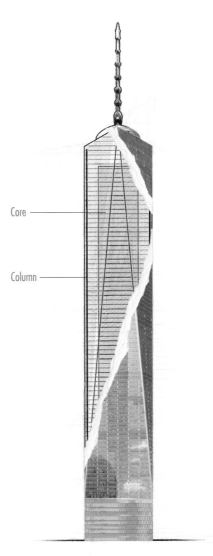

Core

Column

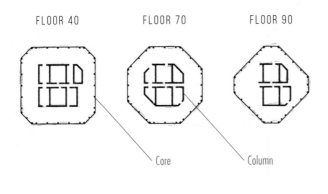

FLOOR 40   FLOOR 70   FLOOR 90

Core   Column

OBSERVATION DECK

The observation decks occupy floors 100 to 102, where there are a couple of restaurants and a cafe. Floor 102's observation deck coincides with the height of the shorter of the original World Trade Center towers, and the glass parapet that extends just above it ends at the same height as the taller tower.

417.0 m

415.1 m

NORTH TOWER

SOUTH TOWER

DESIGN EVOLUTION

After an open competition to select a design for the new building, Daniel Libeskind was selected as the winner. His ideas evolved as requested by the developer, and fused with those of David Childs, who was brought on board at a later date. In the end, the final design bore little resemblance to Libeskind's original plan.

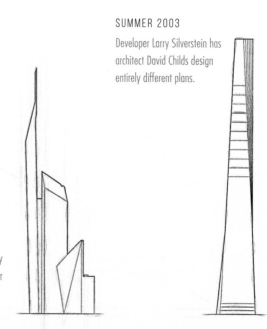

SUMMER 2003

Developer Larry Silverstein has architect David Childs design entirely different plans.

WINTER 2002

Early designs by Libeskind showed a building with a nearly freestanding spire, whose upper reaches would be filled with trees and plants.

SPIRE

The original design features a spire enclosed within a protective radome so that the building tops out at the significant height of 1 776 feet. This was replaced by a bare antenna in 2012 that would be kept upright by using a ring of cables. In part this was down to cost. The antenna was made in several parts that were hoisted up separately, and is crowned with a glass-covered beacon.

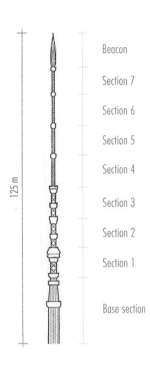

125 m

Beacon

Section 7

Section 6

Section 5

Section 4

Section 3

Section 2

Section 1

Base section

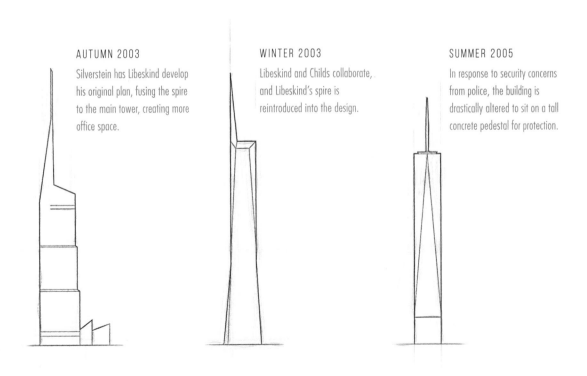

AUTUMN 2003

Silverstein has Libeskind develop his original plan, fusing the spire to the main tower, creating more office space.

WINTER 2003

Libeskind and Childs collaborate, and Libeskind's spire is reintroduced into the design.

SUMMER 2005

In response to security concerns from police, the building is drastically altered to sit on a tall concrete pedestal for protection.

CONSTRUCTION:
2011–16

HEIGHT:
555.7 M

SEOUL
SOUTH KOREA

LOTTE WORLD TOWER

Lotte is one of the largest business conglomerates in South Korea, well known for its shopping malls, hotels and amusement parks, as well as other industries such as construction, IT and financial services. Much like its parent company, the mixed-use Lotte World Tower is host to a diverse array of services. As is common, the retail levels are accessed from the lobby, above which are offices, a luxury hotel, observation decks and officetels. Officetels are common in South Korean real estate, and are a convenient means of studio accommodation for people who work in the offices in the building, as well as the building's staff. They often provide services routinely found in hotels such as gym access and a security desk, and tend to come ready furnished.

The aesthetic of the tower is a mix of modern, sleek, glassy architecture, and Korean influences such as porcelain, ceramics and calligraphy. Despite the vision of the developers, and the elegance of form that the tower was to take, permission to proceed with the development was a long time coming. To obtain the building permit took the conglomerate fifteen years, and was only given on the condition that they paid to reconstruct a nearby runway, so that military aircraft would not be in danger of hitting the tower on their approach.

The giant, but graceful, 123-storey building was completed by the end of 2016, triumphantly entering the top five of the world's tallest buildings.

STRUCTURE

The concrete raft that Lotte World Tower sits on is 6.5 m deep, which in turn is supported by 1-metre-thick concrete piles. The reinforced concrete core is positioned centrally among the eight concrete megacolumns and additional steel columns, connected to each other via three-storey-tall outriggers hidden in the mechanical floors of the structure. The megacolumns are vertical until just beyond the office floors, when they start to taper inwards, terminating at floor 86. Beyond this point, the structural columns are made from steel until the roof at 497 m, and the rest of the building's open crown supports itself through its diagrid construction.

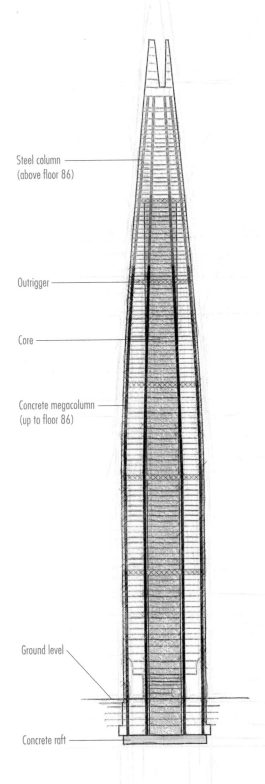

Steel column
(above floor 86)

Outrigger

Core

Concrete megacolumn
(up to floor 86)

Ground level

Concrete raft

STRUCTURE PLAN

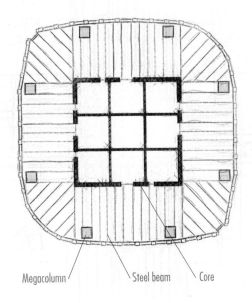

Megacolumn   Steel beam   Core

TALLEST ON THE KOREAN PENINSULA

The Lotte World Tower is the tallest building on the Korean peninsula, surpassing the height of neighbouring North Korea's Ryugyong Hotel. Construction began on Ryugyong Hotel back in 1987, but due to the country's financial difficulties work has not been completed on the building, though the structure is topped out.

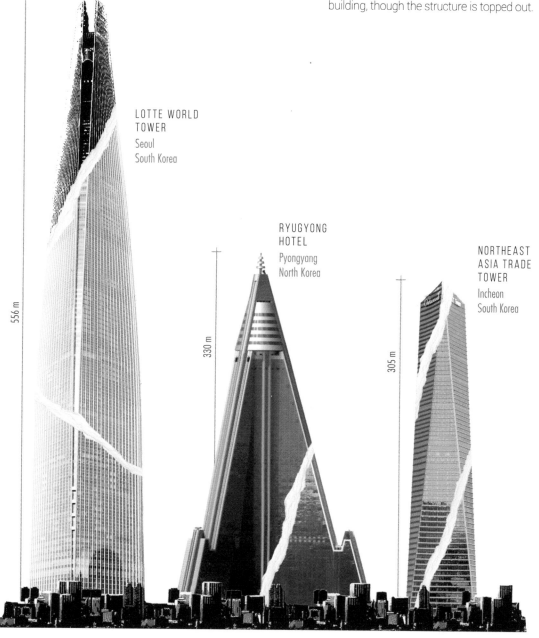

LOTTE WORLD TOWER
Seoul
South Korea

556 m

RYUGYONG HOTEL
Pyongyang
North Korea

330 m

NORTHEAST ASIA TRADE TOWER
Incheon
South Korea

305 m

Observation decks

High-end offices

Hotel

Hotel amenities

Residential/officetel

Office

Lobby/retail

FORM AND FUNCTION

The tower's simple, elegant appearance could be said to be misleading, for the building serves a multitude of functions. Two opposite corners of the building plan are recessed, while the other two are gently curved. As the building gains height the recesses widen, and by the time they reach the crown they leave a broad gap. A glass-bottomed observation deck protrudes from between the gap at the crown – the highest of its kind in the world.

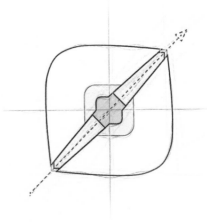

OLD SEOUL

The seams that run up the building, created by the recessed corners, line up with the direction of the old centre of Seoul.

HIGHEST BUILDING WITH GLASS FLOOR

The Lotte World Tower's observation deck is the highest (above ground level) glass-bottomed observatory anywhere in the world. There is a glass-bottomed deck that extends out over the Grand Canyon, around 1 100 m above the Colorado River at its base. However, due to the craggy canyon edge, the point directly below the deck is much closer.

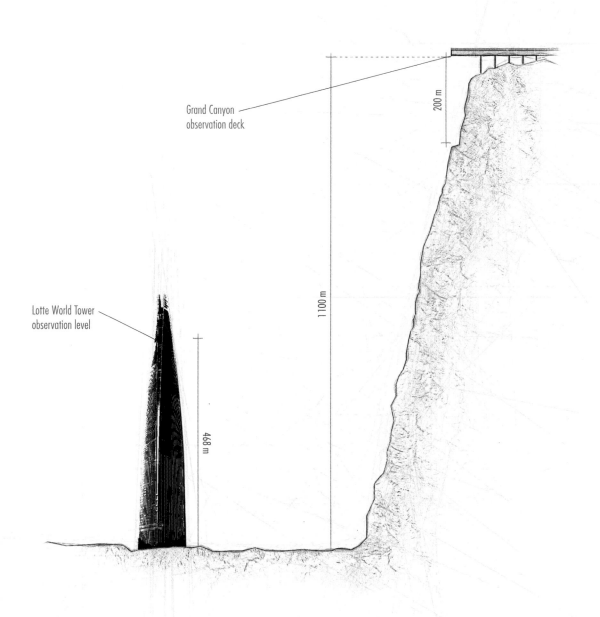

Grand Canyon observation deck

200 m

1 100 m

Lotte World Tower observation level

468 m

ACKNOWLEDGEMENTS

Many thanks to the team at Wildfire, especially Alex Clarke, Ella Gordon and Kate Stephenson. Your input on the book has been hugely appreciated, and has kept me focussed. Thank You!

Thanks to Richard Benjamin from Ditherington Flax Mill for taking the time out to give me a hand. Check out the historic building's website at: http://www.flaxmill-maltings.co.uk.

SOURCES

1001 Buildings You Must See Before You Die by Mark Irving
Cassell Illustrated, 2007

A History of Architecture in 100 Buildings by Dan Cruickshank
William Collins, 2015

A World History of Architecture by Michael Fazio, Marian Moffett, Lawrence Wodehouse
Laurence King Publishing Ltd, 2013

Archi-Graphic by Frank Jacobus
Laurence King Publishing Ltd, 2015

Architectural Details by Emily Cole
Ivy Press, 2002

Architecture – A Visual History by Jonathan Glancey
Dorling Kindersley Limited, 2017

Engineers – From the Great Pyramids to Spacecraft by Adam Hart-Davis
Dorling Kindersley Limited, 2012

Great Buildings – The World's Architectural Masterpieces Explored and Explained by Philip Wilkinson
Dorling Kindersley Limited, 2012

How To Build a Skyscraper by John Hill
RotoVision, 2017

Skyscrapers – A History of the World's Most Extraordinary Buildings by Judith Dupre
Black Dog & Leventhal Publishers, 2013

The Age of Spectacle by Tom Dyckhoff
Random House Books, 2017

Wonders of World Architecture by Neil Parkin
Thames and Hudson, 2002

IMAGE CREDITS

ZACK SCOTT

Zack joined the Royal Air Force at the age of twenty, where he worked as an aircraft technician for several years. He then returned to civilian life to work on high-speed trains, before pursuing his lifelong passion for design. Zack achieved his degree in Graphic Design in 2013 and has since worked inhouse for a couple of companies, before going freelance. His keen interest in science and space lead him to create his first book, *Apollo*, which was published in 2017. *Scrapers*, his second book, is along a similar vein, in that it unites data and graphics to create a visually appealing reading experience.

First published in 2018
by WILDFIRE
An imprint of HEADLINE PUBLISHING GROUP

1

Cataloguing in Publication Data is available from the British Library

ISBN 978 1 4722 4789 6

Illustrations © Zack Scott, unless otherwise indicated

Printed and bound in China by
1010 Printing UK Ltd.

Headline's policy is to use papers that are natural, renewable and recyclable products and made from wood grown in well-
managed forests and other controlled sources. The logging and manufacturing processes are expected to conform to the
environmental regulations of the country of origin.

HEADLINE PUBLISHING GROUP
An Hachette UK Company
Carmelite House
50 Victoria Embankment
London EC4Y 0DZ

www.headline.co.uk
www.hachette.co.uk